Earthshaping E...

Earthshaping Earthkeeping

A DOCTRINE OF CREATION

John Weaver

LYNX

FOR

Megan and Fred

my late parents who encouraged me in

understanding life, nature, and faith

First published in Great Britain in 1999
Lynx Communications
Society for Promoting Christian Knowledge
Holy Trinity Church, Marylebone Road
London NW1 4DU

Bible quotations are from the *New International Version, Inclusive Language Edition*
© Hodder & Stoughton 1995, 1996
The author and publisher acknowledge with thanks permission to reproduce the
following material:
'Decreation', in *Up to Date, Poems 1968–1982*, Steve Turner.
Hodder & Stoughton, 1983.
'Almighty God, Creator...', in *The Whole Earth Shall Cry Glory*, Rev. George
F. MacLeod. Wild Goose Publications, The Iona Community, Glasgow, 1985.

Unless otherwise indicated, Bible quotations are taken from the *New International
Version*, Inclusive Language Edition (Hodder & Stoughton, London, 1995, 1996)

The poem 'Decreation' by Steve Turner, from his book *Up to Date: Poems 1968–1982*
(1983), is reproduced by permission of Hodder & Stoughton Ltd.
The prayer 'Almighty God, Creator...' by the Revd. George F. MacLeod, from his
book *The Whole Earth Shall Cry Glory* (1985), is reproduced by permission of
Wild Goose Publications, The Iona Community, Glasgow.

British Library Cataloguing-in-Publication Data

A catalogue record for this book is available from the British Library

ISBN 1-901443-11-6

Typeset by Wilmaset Ltd, Birkenhead, Wirral
Printed in Great Britain by Redwood Books, Trowbridge, Wiltshire

Contents

Acknowledgements

I am grateful to Tim Bradshaw, Michael Humphreys, and Rex Mason, my colleagues at Regent's Park College, and to Keith Ward at Christ Church, for their comments and advice on the first draft of the manuscript.

I acknowledge with thanks Regent's Park College and their Study Guide Series editor, Paul Fiddes, for permission to reproduce Figure 2, which originally appeared in my previous work: *In the Beginning God: Modern Science and the Christian Doctrine of Creation* (Macon, Smyth & Helwys, Regent's Park College, Oxford, 1994).

Finally, I am most grateful to my wife Sheila, who is my best critic, careful proof reader (of sense, understanding, grammar, and spelling) and patient partner in research and ministry.

How to Get the Best Out of This Book

We explore the meaning and purpose of the world and universe, of which we are a part, through Scripture, church tradition, and science. To do this we consider the creation stories of the people of Israel; the stories of their Near Eastern neighbours; and the developing scientific picture of the universe, and the place of our earth within it. Through bringing these stories together, we explore a holistic understanding of creation, and a theological appreciation of the creator God, who calls us into a covenant relationship.

The scope of the text

We begin with a consideration of the setting in which Israel began to think and reflect theologically about creation. We set these reflections against the background of Near Eastern mythology, before exploring the Old Testament accounts of creation. Throughout Part I we focus on the question: what sort of God is revealed? The emphasis is on God as the unique, transcendent, divine, and morally faithful creator, who brings about an ordered world, with human beings in the image of God, and in relationship with God. The Old Testament understanding of creation presents us with a courageous proclamation of Israel's faith in God, in the face of the competing religious outlooks of the nations around them. This was especially true at the time of the Exile, when they had been subjugated through the Babylonian conquest of Judah. Here Israel's story has a propaganda role, establishing Yahweh as the one true God of creation and of world history.

Throughout the Old Testament passages we discover the importance of relationships: with God, with human beings, and with creation. The culmination of these relationships is expressed in worship. Moving into Part II we discover not only worship and awe in the face of scientific discovery, but also features of broken relationships, seen both in scientific disasters and human self-centredness.

Part II concentrates on the stories of science, and develops two important issues: boundary questions which mark the limits of scientific understanding; and the apparent design of the universe, exemplified by 'fine tuning' and the anthropic principle. These issues lead us back to the question: what sort of God is being revealed? We will discover that the finely tuned nature of the physical laws that brought the universe into being lead some scientists to speak of 'design'. Yet rather than evoke a designer, cosmologists seek a Grand Unified Theory, which will explain the origin of the universe in purely scientific terms. Other cosmologists, irrespective of belief, have recognized humanity as an integral part of the universe – the Anthropic Principle. Thus we find that the discoveries of modern cosmology are not inconsistent with the conclusion of faith that there is a God-given purpose to the universe.

As the nature of the universe is more carefully explored, we recognize that we do not have a ready-made universe, but rather the picture of an emerging creation. We discover this through the evolutionary model, displaying a God-given fruitfulness, fertility and development. We also recognize that there is an interconnectedness to creation, a holism that cannot be ignored either in terms of an evolving universe, or of the place of humanity within creation. The results of scientific enquiry take us on a long journey of discovery into the origins of the universe, they reveal evidence that we may use in discussing the immanence of God, but the journey reaches its limit; there are boundary questions that science cannot answer. These are questions of meaning and purpose, which move us to consider the transcendent God of faith.

In Part III we try to make sense of the stories, focusing on the transcendence and immanence of God, as revealed through boundary questions, the anthropic principle, and through the Hebrew Scriptures. We recognize that as a result of human activity environmental disasters have occurred, leading us to understand the broken nature of the covenant relationship. We explore a theology for earthkeeping, which brings us firmly back to the question: what sort of God is the God of creation? From these perspectives we develop a doctrine of creation, seeking to understand the nature of the God who is testified to both in Scripture and in scientific discovery: a God who is both immanent and transcendent; a God of covenantal relationship; a God who is trinitarian in nature; and a creation that is holistic, to be redeemed, and is involved in the worship of its creator.

Some key issues that we will consider through the text

Covenant

The expression of God's relationship with creation in terms of covenant is explored in Chapter 3, where the biblical passages, especially Genesis 6—9, are discussed. The nature of God's covenant, and the need for human beings to understand this relationship, is further developed in Chapter 8, where we consider the environment and human responsibility for creation. The Bible points us to see God as the source of order, and to see God intimately involved with creation. The Genesis account of creation reveals that God has put relationship at the heart of the universe. We recognize that science operates on the assumption of an ordered world, but we realize that the world's order is contingent, it could have been otherwise. We will propose that this universe is the choice of a creator, who chooses a contingent universe that expresses his nature: love, freedom, and relationship; and a universe, so created, that can respond to its creator.

We understand God as both transcendent, in bringing creation into being, and immanent in the evolving development of the universe and of life on earth. We will maintain that it is in the incarnation of God in Christ that we are supremely pointed towards God's dynamic and intimate relationship with the world. Here we find the fullest expression of God's immanence.

Fine tuning and the anthropic principle

The recognition by modern cosmologists of the fine tuning of the initial conditions of the universe, and of the integral place of human beings within the universe – the anthropic principle – is considered in detail in Chapters 4 and 5, and reflected upon theologically in Part III, especially in Chapter 7.

The anthropic principle states that we see the universe the way it is because if it were different, we would not be here to observe it. In its weak form it says, to 'explain' why the Big Bang took place ten thousand million years ago, that it takes that long for intelligent beings to evolve. In its strong version it maintains that the development of the universe had to be the way it is for us to be here. The laws of science, as we know them, reveal fundamental values, such as the size of the electric charge of the electron or the ratio of masses of proton and electron, which appear to have been finely adjusted to make the development of life a possibility.

Such evidence supports the strong anthropic principle, or can even be construed as evidence of divine purpose in creation. From an ecological view, it is claimed that the climate and chemical properties of the earth, throughout history, have always been optimal for life. We will also suggest that evolution requires a guiding principle to prevent evolutionary changes running down so many blind alleys.

The recognition of such an anthropic principle with its supportive fine tuning is a revival of the design argument. The nature of the initial conditions of a Big Bang, the interconnectedness of the fundamental forces and laws of the universe, the existence of human beings, and the mystery of the human mind with personality, lends credence to the suggestion of the existence of a designer God.

The step of faith, however, lies in moving from design and purpose to belief in a creator whose mind and purpose are written into the evolution of human life.

Boundary questions

Throughout Part II, and again in Chapter 7, we will draw attention to the limits of scientific knowledge, and raise the questions that science is not equipped to answer. Science is providing us with many answers to the nature of life, and of the universe, but the questions relating to ultimate meaning remain. These we identify as *boundary questions* – they are not answered by research into the component parts of the universe and the stuff of life, but can only be answered at a higher level. For example, we will maintain that biological evolution requires a higher level of explanation that only theology can give, if we are to find any meaning within creation. So, while science deals with the minutiae of particles and the mega theories of the universe's origin, theology attempts to pull the whole of human experience together, producing an holistic view of the universe, in which we find our existence. Theology meets the boundary questions raised by a finely tuned universe with talk of the God whose purpose is revealed in Scripture, and supremely in Jesus Christ.

Transcendence and immanence

Throughout the whole book we discover the nature of a God who is both beyond and within creation, who is both transcendent, bringing creation into being, and immanent, enjoying its fruitfulness and suffering with its brokenness. From the perspective of science we discover a dynamic planet with a beginning and a long history. We recognize an organic and holistic worldview, in which there are dynamic connections between the physico-chemical environment and the variety of life forms, as well as within the living environment itself. From a theological perspective we will discuss the transcendent God who brings creation into being, and the immanent God who involves himself in the risk of creation, which has a love-given freedom.

Cosmology helps us to understand the magnitude and careful purpose that is to be found within the universe, and so helps us to know something of the power and care of God. The evolutionary model of the universe and of life encourages us to develop an immanent view of God, who has journeyed with creation, and suffers with the consequences of giving freedom to creation. We conclude that God is seen as transcendent creator, yet is immanent in the history of the people; and God shares a covenant relationship with people, which is characterized by grace. Immanence is understood through the development of the whole universe, ecological relationships, and the evolution of life. We understand God as trinity, and recognize the supreme place of God's immanence in the incarnation of Christ. The continuing presence of God, within creation, is as Spirit.

The universe is seen as sacramental: it is the visible expression of the invisible God. It is the place where God is revealed, and where all creation is invited to respond in worship.

See page xiv for a diagrammatic representation of the text.

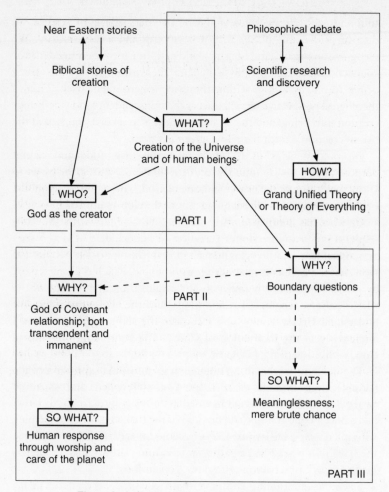

Figure 1. A diagrammatic representation of the text

Introduction

This is a book that focuses on stories, and so it seems appropriate to begin with my own story. When I was nine years old I remember wondering about exactly where the universe might be. Could I liken the universe to our goldfish pond – was the universe a pond in God's back garden?

Growing up in a loving Christian home, I naturally had God in the equation of my thinking about the world in which I lived.

My father taught biology and at an early age he introduced me to many exciting aspects of the biological sciences. He named the plants and animals that I encountered in the garden or in the countryside, and I learned their correct Latin names, species and genera, and something of the classification of the plant and animal kingdoms. In our pond we had frogs and I enjoyed the spring time when we watched frogspawn develop through the various stages of tadpole to adult frog. I learned about caterpillars becoming chrysalids and then moths or butterflies. My father had a microscope at home and he showed me that tap water was teeming with microscopic life (which did not encourage me to drink it!) and that the hairs of my head had a particular structure. The scientist in me was being shaped: observation, questions, conclusions.

Scientific questioning continued with chemical experiments in my early teens: growing copper sulphate crystals and halite crystals. But all this experimentation was brought to an abrupt end with experiments with rocket fuel when I was about 12 years of age. I began making an explosive rocket fuel out of sugar, sulphur and potassium chlorate. Finding that the aluminium cigar tubes of my father's Christmas presents melted before my rockets could get going, I searched around for something stronger – a small carbon dioxide gas cylinder for a soda syphon. I cut off the end, rammed in the rocket fuel, set it up on the window sill at the back of the house, and lit the fuse!!

It took off perfectly, cleared the side of my parents' bungalow, but then exploded (the hole was too small for the gases to escape). There was a loud bang followed by the sound of breaking glass (it had blown in our neighbour's window).

1961 saw two revolutions in my thinking and questioning. In the spring of 1961 the school Scientific Society presented a geology lecture: rocks, minerals, and fossils. The speaker ended his talk by showing us 'potato stones' from the Triassic rocks of Penarth, near Cardiff. These were concretions, about the size of a large potato, which were filled with crystals. He offered to break one open and invited someone to come and see. I volunteered; as he broke it open he said, 'You are the first person to see inside this nodule since the moment it was formed, in fact, ever!' From that moment I was hooked; geology was to dominate my interest through school, university, and my first employment as a lecturer in geology. However, I was soon to learn that geology as a scientific discipline is limited by both space and time in the factual information that it presents, for rocks are deep below us in the Earth's crust and geological time extends back some 4,500 million years.

The world of living things in its variety, development, and microscopic form became ever more fascinating when, as a young amateur geologist, I began to discover the world of fossils. I collected brachiopods (sea shells) and trilobites, long extinct, from quarries near my home. On coal tips I discovered fossil ferns, leaves, tree roots, and tree trunks, extinct plant life that was the origin of the coal that, at that time, heated our home. It was a journey of discovery, almost like a detective story, as I began to understand something of the rich variety of life on our planet, and especially as I came to recognize that the nature of this life had changed with time. I was of course travelling a journey that others had travelled before me, and I was benefiting from their discoveries and research.

Studying geology in the late 1960s was exciting as the implications of the theory of plate tectonics (the model of the Earth's crust made up of six plates which move apart, alongside, and under each other, the margins of these plates being marked by volcanic and earthquake activity) for the evolution of the Earth's crust began to unfold. This was a conceptual revolution that would shape the future of geology. My own research and teaching over the next ten years was focused on this area: geotectonics and structural geology.

Back in 1961, in the autumn, a second revolution took place in my life, when I made a personal profession of faith in Christ. The warm loving faith of Christian parents was something that then became my own personal experience. However, as with geology, so too for theology and faith there are no certain proofs of statements made by the church, and often we are again limited by space and time. The transcendent God is beyond the universe of our experience, and the Christian faith is anchored in events some 2,000 years ago.

For 17 years these two strands of my life, geology and Christian faith, would run alongside each other, only occasionally intersecting. Throughout this period I had been like Francis Bacon looking through my geological studies at the 'works of God', and through my church life and personal faith at the 'words of God'. Or, as a number of early scientists were described, I lived with 'the book of God in one hand and the book of Nature in the other'.

But another dramatic change was about to take place. My understanding of the spiritual journey went through a conceptual revolution, when I recognized that the Christian faith was to be lived out in seven-day-a-week discipleship and not only when the church met together. As George Herbert wrote in his hymn, 'King of glory, King of peace':

Seven whole days, not one in seven,
I will praise Thee.

My faith and my teaching and research in geology were part of a whole and I needed to avoid the dualism of a 'Sunday faith' and a secular occupation.

In Part I we shall look at the people of Israel, their experience of the world in which they lived, and their faith-experience of the Covenant God, which enabled them to see, in stark contrast to their pagan neighbours, creation as God's creation. In Part II we shall look at the conceptual revolutions that have taken place in the world of science and our understanding of the universe and this planet on which we live. We will also consider the role that natural theology has in shaping our faith and our perception of the world. The conceptual revolutions in science have had a profound effect on the way in which creation is understood. We move from Aquinas and his 'proofs' for the Christian God as creator of the universe, to the theistic views of Isaac Newton, to the atheistic position of Thomas Huxley and, more recently, Richard Dawkins, before returning to the deism and panentheism of some modern cosmologists and ecologists. We shall ask what sort of God is revealed by scientific studies, and recognize the dangers of anthropocentrism.

The recognition of a seven-day-a-week faith encouraged me to look again at the relationship of work in science, my family life, and my belief in the Bible, in particular the biblical account of creation. I was well aware in the 1970s of the juxtaposition of Bible and science that many found a problem. For many people the Genesis account of creation is a stumbling block. According to David Wilkinson,[1] a survey of British teenagers in the early 1990s showed that one third of those who rejected Christianity did so because they thought that Christians believed in a seven-day creation about 6,000 years ago, a picture that was contrary to all that they had learned and understood through science. I have found through leading sessions on apologetics in schools, colleges, and at the British annual Christian festival, Spring Harvest, that a similar explanation for rejecting Christianity is given by many adults. Behind this lies a lack of understanding of the creation account in Genesis. There may also, on the part of some, be an ostrich approach to the discoveries of science, which is an indication of dualism between life and faith, where faith and work do not question each other.

Another revolution in my own life came in the form of God's call to pastoral ministry, and after three years' theological study at Oxford I began ministry as a Baptist minister in Northamptonshire. Here in the everyday ministry of the church, faith and life cannot be kept apart. Faith in the creator of heaven and earth, faith in God incarnate in Jesus Christ, faith in God present in the church and individual lives through his Holy Spirit, has to be worked out in the nitty-gritty of human life: birth, growth, conversion, commitment, doubt, anxiety, marriage, suffering, and death. There can be no hiding in the laboratory nor the seminary. The universe, the world of our everyday experience, and our personal lives, are brought together, if we will allow them so to be.

Returning to Oxford as a tutor in pastoral theology has allowed me the privilege of theological reflection, asking the 'God questions' in all areas of life. I believe that the key questions that we should hold at the front of our minds when looking at the world and aspects of faith are:

1 What does this teach us about God?
2 How does this help us to understand how God works in the world and through human lives?
3 What might this suggest about God's desire for us, for our community, and for our world?

An award from the John Templeton Science and Religion Programme has allowed me to explore the dialogue between science and Christian faith. Scientific and biblical models for understanding creation had an important place in these discussions. In Part III we shall look at the Christian perspective on creation, and at questions of suffering, and stewardship of the environment; and I shall present a doctrine of creation for our life in the universe today.

My life has been a journey of discovery and of conceptual revolutions in both science and faith, and in my experience of life. I am sure that we have not heard the final word from the scientific arena; there will be further discoveries to aid our understanding of creation. Equally, I am sure that we will receive further reflection from theologians upon creation and the relationship of human beings with their world. We still have much to learn, and we will keep active in our quest for understanding.

1 *The Jews in Babylon Tell the Story of Creation*

By the rivers of Babylon we sat and wept
when we remembered Zion.[1]

The background to the story

When Israel proclaimed its creation faith, recorded in Genesis 1.1—2.4, she was in the darkest period of her history, in exile in Babylonia. The removal of the leadership of Judah to Babylon at the beginning of the sixth century BC was a body blow to the nationhood and religious life of Israel. The Exile is a watershed in Israelite history. In the space of 23 years we move from the restored national pride, extended boundaries of the state, and exclusive worship of Yahweh under Josiah (640–609 BC), to the invasion and conquest of Israel by the Babylonian army under Nebuchadnezzar, and the subsequent destruction of Jerusalem with its Temple, and the deportations to Babylon. That this did not mark the end of the story is of itself a surprise, but that this was a time when Israel's faith was reworked and strengthened is truly amazing.

In 597 BC Nebuchadnezzar's army left Judah in ruins. Archaeological evidence suggests that most of the fortified cities were burned to the ground. The king, Jehoiachin, and many of the political and religious leaders were taken and interned in Babylon, where Jehoiachin was held under house arrest, while retaining the title of King of Judah. Zedekiah, a puppet king, was left to rule Judah on behalf of the Babylonian captors. In 587 BC rebellion led to the return of Nebuchadnezzar's army, this uprising was ruthlessly put down, the leaders killed, Jerusalem destroyed, the Temple burned to the ground, and there was a second deportation of leaders to Babylon. With the assassination of the Babylonian governor, Gedaliah, all hope was extinguished, and there was a third deportation to Babylon in 582 BC, probably as a reprisal for the chaos following his murder.

Life in Judah after the destruction of Jerusalem was probably harsh, although there is a lack of information about this period. Most of the natural leaders had been deported, many people had died in battle or of disease and starvation, and many others had fled. Lamentations presents us with a picture of life that was miserable and precarious.[2] Religion was, not surprisingly, undermined by the destruction of the Temple and there was probably a return to the syncretistic religious practices that marked the period before the accession of Josiah. However, John Bright believes that it is likely that the Temple remained 'holy ground', possibly a place of pilgrimage.[3] It is also possible that the Deuteronomist History went through its final redaction in Judah during this period – evidence that religious faith and theological reflection on the nation's life had not been destroyed.

Nevertheless, the cream of the nation's political, intellectual and religious leadership had been deported to Babylon. The total for the three deportations amounted to about 4,600,[4] but if these were all adult males, then the figure was probably nearer 12–15,000 people, which would have represented something like five per cent of the population of Judah. But these, suggests Bright, would shape Israel's future,

> both giving to her faith its new direction and providing the impulse for the ultimate restoration of the Jewish community in Palestine.[5]

The experience of the Jews in exile may not have been intolerably harsh. They weren't prisoners, but neither were they free. They were slaves of the state, without any right of appeal. Nevertheless, Jeremiah's letter to the exiles[6] suggests that life may have continued with a degree of normality – building houses, planting gardens, and bringing up families. Ezekiel's account, near the beginning of the exile (594–571 BC),[7] would suggest that the exiles were in settled communities of their own,[8] and maybe coming together for worship. For some, life in Babylon might also have been an opportunity to grow rich. Our knowledge is fairly scanty for this period, and it is probable that the people suffered oppression and ill-treatment from time to time, as they would always have been subject to the whim of the Babylonian government and its local representatives. If the books of Daniel and Esther, irrespective of their dates of writing, reflect this period in Israel's history, then all was not sweetness and light for the exiles. Psalm 137 reflects both the despair and dereliction felt by the exiles (1–6), and despite reasonable treatment, a deep hatred of their captors (8–9). This same bleak message is seen in Ezekiel's vision of dry, lifeless bones.[9]

Whatever their physical circumstances, their religious beliefs had taken a severe beating. We must remember that nationhood, national identity and pride, went hand in hand with these beliefs. So it is to the faith of the people in exile that we now turn.

A faith to hold on to

Rex Mason helpfully presents the major question for the exilic community: 'Since Yahwism before the exile had been so much the official religion of the Davidic nation state, how was it to be defined and understood now?'[10] They were stateless, and the covenants with Abraham and David appeared to be in tatters; fundamentally, Yahweh had deserted them. But it was her faith in Yahweh that had called Israel into being; could this faith prevent her total annihilation, even now? This was a theological emergency, for the cult had been dealt a mortal blow. The status of Israel's God was thrown into question, for in a time when it was believed that each nation had a god, Israel's God had apparently fallen to the power of the gods of Babylonia. There would probably have been a wholesale loss of faith on the part of the people, and, therefore, a theological explanation was urgently required.

In his book *Hopeful Imagination*, Walter Brueggemann[11] presents a view of the pivotal nature of the exile: it is the end of the known world and marks its 'relinquishment', and the 'reception' of a new world given by God through his prophets, Jeremiah, Ezekiel, and Deutero-Isaiah. Israel must let go of the old world of king and Temple, which God has removed, and look for the new world that he is preparing for them.[12]

Jeremiah and Ezekiel explain the exile largely in terms of Yahweh's judgement on Israel's sin, with the hope of a purged future, a new covenant, a new community, beyond exile. This would be Yahweh's ultimate restoration of the people.[13] For Ezekiel, the one fixed point in the midst of the upheaval of the nation's life is the sovereign majesty of God, beyond human reach, who claims obedience and radical conversion of all life. God's purpose in his dealings with Israel is that they shall know that he is God.[14] It is Yahweh who is able to bring life out of death through the wind of his life-giving Spirit.[15] Isaiah stresses the powerful word of God, which has the final say in history, both Israel's and the nations of the world. This confident proclamation forms the 'book ends' of his prophetic work.[16] God's purposes will be achieved whatever power battles or alliances are made: kingdoms may rise and fall but the word of God endures for ever. Yahweh speaks and his will is fulfilled; his is the word that liberates Israel and which creates the world,[17] but the Babylonian gods remain silent and Isaiah taunts them.[18]

It is the Priestly writers (P) who take up the theme of the power of the word of Yahweh, as they introduce the history and law of Israel, presented as the Pentateuch. They attempted a major redefinition of Israel's faith, written during the exile and possibly completed in the rebuilt temple. They set out to write a history of the earliest experiences of their nation, starting from creation itself and culminating in the Covenant on Mount Sinai. Mason describes their work as representing 'a bold and theologically creative attempt to renew Yahwism as a living religion after all its major institutions had collapsed'.[19] They drew on the riches of their national heritage and religious traditions, believing that new hope would emerge from the lessons of their history; with the recognition in that story of the pattern of sin, repentance, and restoration. Bright suggests that their community was based on Sabbath observance, which was seen as a test of their obedience to the Covenant[20] and a sign instituted with creation.[21]

We now begin to see the context for the creation story of Genesis 1. It forms the opening pages of Israel's redefinition of her faith in Yahweh, when all seemed to be lost. As such it is a brave affirmation in the face of a great weight of contrary evidence. Their account of creation, in which God is the one and only creator of all that exists, presents a polemic against the Egyptian, Canaanite, and especially Babylonian accounts of creation.

The polemic they presented

So we can let the Jews in Babylon tell the story of creation.

The people of Israel had been in exile in Babylonia for a number of years, and their situation was depressing in every way. They were aliens in a foreign land, with a different culture, different religion, and different climate and environment from their own. On top of this they were prisoners with an existence that was not far from slavery. The understanding of their captors was that the gods of Babylon were victorious over the God of Israel, and they were often tempted into believing this version of the truth. One community were living in mud-brick houses alongside the irrigation channel, called the River Chebar, in an inhospitable climate and land. They had been granted permission by their overlords to establish their homes, and they had sought to bring a degree of order and meaning to their existence. The local inhabitants made fun of their plight and derided their religion. Spiritually they were depressed. Their Temple in Jerusalem, the place where they had believed that God dwelt in a special way, was over a thousand kilometres away, and worse still, it was in ruins. Their view was that they were far away from God, and that their very condition demonstrated his impotence. Ezekiel and Isaiah of Babylon declared that God was not confined to the land of Israel and the Temple in Jerusalem, but was with them in Babylon, and he was ready to forgive them and bring about a new Exodus.

It is in this context that the writers of Genesis 1 began to reflect upon the faith of Israel. This priestly writer, or group of writers, reflected upon the traditions of their faith, the writings that the religious community had preserved and brought with them into exile, and upon the history of God's dealings with his people; they thought about the story of God's relationship with them over the years, from the Patriarchs to Egypt, from the Exodus to David, and from Solomon's Temple to the Exile. To this they added their experience of the world, and the religious views held by their Babylonian captors. The writers took all these experiences, and, through their faith in Yahweh, a newly edited version of the Scriptures took shape. The very first belief that they wanted to express was that the covenant God of Israel was the God of all creation. Out of their experience they opened their major work with what we now know as Genesis 1:

> In the beginning God created the heavens and the earth ... And God said ... And God said ... God saw all that he had made, and it was very good.

Through Genesis 1—11 creation is linked with the history of Israel as God's chosen people, beginning with Abraham; the God of the covenant, the sustainer and redeemer of Israel, is the creator of the universe.

Although there are certainly points of contact between Genesis 1—11 and the Babylonian creation epic (as we shall discover in Chapters 2 and 3), there is a profound difference between the struggles of Marduk with Tiamat and the Genesis 1 narrative. It may not be fair to try to make comparisons, as we would not be comparing like with like. Gordon Wenham notes, for example, that *Enuma elish* is concerned to glorify the god Marduk; the creative acts simply illustrating his power.[22] The Priestly writers were also probably familiar with the Egyptian accounts of creation, but the significance of Genesis 1 is the way in which they use other accounts; and it is illuminating to see how these other accounts of creation were modified.

Thus Claus Westermann[23] states that while P follows the example of presenting creation in a succession of generations – important in Egyptian, Sumerian, and Babylonian accounts – P has no genealogy of the gods. P rejects the struggle motif and the births of the gods, and instead presents creation as God's act of making, and as the decree of God's word; these writers are monotheists. Wenham[24] concludes from this that Genesis 1 is a deliberate statement of the Hebrew view of creation over against rival views, and that it is a 'polemical repudiation of such myths'. Rival cosmologies are attacked in a number of areas: God created all that is out of nothing,[25] in contrast to the idea of matter existing eternally alongside the gods; the dragons that rival the gods in Canaanite mythology are now seen to be merely the creation of God;[26] the struggle of the gods to divide the waters is replaced by a simple divine decree;[27] the Genesis account avoids naming the sun, moon and stars, which were part of Babylonian astrology. The heavenly bodies are created by God; they are not objects of worship, as they were in other Near Eastern cultures. The sun and moon are for signs and seasons. Mason helpfully suggests that, as with the signs of sabbath (Genesis 2), and rainbow (Genesis 9), these can also be seen as signs of God's relationship, his covenant, with Israel and with all creation.[28] Throughout all this God simply creates, rather than employing mysterious incantations.

In addition there is the place of human beings: in Babylonian tradition they were an afterthought – they have a walk on part as servants of the gods – but in Genesis they are seen as the climax of creation. This and the other features mentioned above represent a deliberate rejection of other cosmologies.

Their faith is strengthened

The stories from the past reminded those in exile of what God had done in the nation's history, that even in times of suffering and rebellion he had not deserted them. The God of salvation was the God of creation, and he was also the God of new beginnings. It is to this hope that the prophets look.

In their redefinition of the faith they have recognized that Yahweh is not confined to Israel; the creator God of Israel's covenant is the God of the universe and the nations. Thus Deutero-Isaiah speaks about God guiding the course of history.

After the death of Nebuchadnezzar in 562 BC life became more unsettled in Babylonia, and was probably more difficult for the exiles as well. After a number of brief reigns, Nabonidus came to the throne in 556 BC. He neglected both the worship of Marduk and also the city of Babylon that housed Marduk's temple, leaving his son Belshazzar as his representative in the capital. He was overthrown in a bloodless invasion in 539 BC by Cyrus of Persia. Cyrus allowed freedom of worship for all the peoples of his empire, and he encouraged displaced people groups to return home.

With the rise of Cyrus events took on more global proportions and might be seen as being beyond little nations with their own deities. Israel's faith would need to be of universal proportions if it was to make sense of the events of history.

Deutero-Isaiah speaks into this situation[29] and looks toward a new exodus.[30] Yahweh, not Marduk, is the creator of the universe[31] and he is sovereign Lord of history[32] and Cyrus is Yahweh's instrument in history. He is the redeeming God of Israel, who can be trusted.[33] This message of salvation applies not only to the exiles,[34] but also to all the nations,[35] to the ends of the earth,[36] the beasts,[37] heaven, earth, mountains and trees.[38]

God is creator and Lord of history;[39] he is doing a new thing;[40] he is proclaiming a new covenant, like that with Noah,[41] like that with David,[42] and redemption through a new exodus.[43] There is, as in the Priestly writers' work, a polemic against the foreign nations and their gods,[44] and the ever-present connection between God's word and events. God predicts the fall of Babylon,[45] which demonstrates his superiority over Marduk.

It is here in the exile that the Jewish faith develops its fullest expression of the uniqueness of God. Clements points to the prohibition of images as the feature that most clearly expresses their monotheism.[46] An image could be thought to convey a degree of access and therefore control over a god. Yahweh is seen to possess freedom and transcendence that would be compromised by such an image. It is interesting to note that in Daniel 3 (set in this historical context), when the three Jewish exiles refuse to bow down to the gold image built by Nebuchadnezzar and in consequence find themselves placed in the 'fiery furnace', they sing a psalm in praise of the God of creation.[47]

A theological reflection on exilic faith

We have recognized that the Genesis account of creation plays an important part in the redefinition of the faith of Israel, as she comes to terms with defeat, destruction, deportation, and exile. We will see in the next chapter that it owes much to the influence of the creation myths of the ancient Near East, which leads us to ask at this point, what sort of account of creation is Genesis 1? If Genesis 1 is not to be taken literally, does it therefore fall into the realm of myths and legends? Ancient stories about creation were all channels of meaning, to help societies cope with their experiences of the world in which they were born, lived, and died. They were not essentially accounts of the observable 'scientific' features of the earth and sky, but rather they were vehicles of the hopes, aspirations, and even fears of people. Cosmologist John Barrow comments:

> The primitive belief in order and in the sequence of cause and effect displayed by myths is consistent with the belief that it is necessary to have some reason for the existence of everything – a reason that pays due respect for the natural forces that hold life and death in their hands.[48]

Ellen van Wolde makes a similar point at the beginning of her exploration of creation stories:

> Without a story about the beginning, human beings face chaos, and their origin seems to be an abyss. In order to provide a foundation for existence, the beginning was filled with meaning. Moreover, every culture attaches a meaning to the beginning, often in the form of stories. These are not stories in the sense of tales, but realities in which people live. These are stories which give people roots.[49]

Such stories, unlike science, are not necessarily factual, but rather, and more importantly, give meaning to the facts. Barrow points out that, whereas the world of experience and observation is bewilderingly plural and complex, most myths represent a primitive and simple causation for the world. They portray the victory of light over dark, the cracking of some cosmic egg, the story of two world parents, or the defeat of monsters by gods.

A creation story presupposes that time began at some point in the past and has continued up until the present. The creation story in Genesis shows the connection between the beginning and what follows. The story gives structure to time. It is precisely by the way in which the story creates a context and makes a connection between events from

8

beginning to end, that events take on meaning, says van Wolde.[50] She is right to conclude that such stories form part of reality, for

> with images expressed in language, and with words which sometimes stand at the very edge of what can still be said or understood, people try to understand something of another reality. For them it is a matter not just of belief, but also of a kind of sense of life.[51]

The first eleven chapters of Genesis tell the story of the primal history of the world. It begins with creation, in primordial time and space. After this the universal history becomes focused into the history of God's chosen people, through Abraham and his descendants.

Stanley Jaki believes that Genesis 1 is conspicuously void of mythical elements:

> the unusually systematic character of Genesis 1 should suggest that it contains a literary device to make very explicit the message about the total dependence of *all* on God. Written as Genesis 1 was in such a way as to instruct and enlighten the uneducated, that device had to be such as to be instinctively grasped by them.[52]

The Priestly (P) and the Yahwist (J) documents, parts of which make up Genesis 1.1—2.3 (P) and 2.4—3.24 (J), are expressing a faith in God's acts of salvation that come through his election, or his free choice to relate himself to people. The faith that is central to these passages is a faith in the God who made a covenant with Abraham, though this God is of course the creator of the world. Gerhard von Rad[53] says that Israel looked back in faith from her own election, to the creation of the world, and Westermann[54] sees creation faith as the spiritual high point of Israel's understanding of her calling. But Brevard Childs finds that Genesis depicts a wider relationship that God establishes with his creatures; he believes that von Rad's subordination of universal history to the particular salvation history of Israel runs into serious literary and theological problems, and concludes that 'the canonical role of Genesis 1—11 testifies to the priority of creation. The divine relation to the world stems from God's initial creative purpose for the universe, not for Israel alone.'[55]

Nevertheless, von Rad's conclusion that the Genesis account is not myth or saga, but priestly doctrine, is attractive. It is ancient, sacred knowledge, which has been preserved and reformed, expanded and reflected upon with the experiences of faith. It is both cosmological and theological knowledge; it is theological reflection upon what faith is able to declare objectively. Von Rad is right to note that it is only in Genesis 1 that we find direct theological statements about creation; he describes this as moving in the realm of 'theological definitions'.[56] It is a profound passage on beginnings and identity, and as such compares with the opening verses of the Gospels according to Mark[57] and according to John.[58]

I will develop an argument that maintains that Genesis 1 presents us with an account of creation which is not only of theological importance, but which is also perceptive of the observable world in which it was written. Through the following chapters we shall consider Genesis 1 and other biblical accounts of creation through the eyes of critical scholarship, but also consider it in the light of modern scientific discovery. It would seem to make sense that if the world, at least in part, reveals the nature of God, then a biblical account of creation, inspired by God, would not only tell us about theological truths, but also something of the observable world.

Genesis 1 is the dramatic opening chapter to both the Jewish and Christian Scriptures. It introduces the creator and his creatures, and sets the scene for the relationship of human beings and God. Genesis 1 is unique, but may still be compared with other passages that reflect the mystery of God's creativity, such as Psalms 8 and 148 or Job 38. It goes beyond these passages in the scope and comprehensiveness of its vision, says Wenham,[59] and in its present form it is a careful literary composition that introduces the narratives that follow. The writer does not primarily attempt or want to explain creation; rather he desires to evoke a wonder in creation that will lead to worship, a proper relation between human beings and their creator.

It is possible to see Genesis 1 as an exilic/post-exilic dynamic worldview, which reveals all that the creator wishes us to know. It should not be dragged out in support of fundamentalist arguments; nor should there be a constant seeking to show how each new scientific discovery supports or denies its truth. It is not that form of literature. Jaki concludes:

> Although that majestic chapter could have lost its credibility through the endless series of interpretations given to it as age followed age, it has retained a unique appeal through the ages in proof of its intrinsic soundness. This alone should commend its superhuman quality and origin.[60]

We have discovered, as Brueggemann declares, that creation is not careless, casual, or accidental; it is God's intention[61] – creation embodies an obedient unity. God creates by speaking in ways that finally will be heard. 'His word has the authority of suffering compassion.' We see in the early chapters the troubled relation of creator/creation and God's enduring resolve to have creation on his terms. As we move into the history of the special people of Israel, 'still to be settled is the way in which the world will come to terms with the purposes of God, willingly assenting to be God's good creation.' Because this remains unresolved and the relationship unsettled, the message is one of promise.[62]

2 The Creation Stories Told by the Babylonians and Others

> To whom, then, will you compare God?
> What image will you compare him to?
> As for an idol, a metal worker casts it,
> and a goldsmith overlays it with gold
> and fashions silver chains for it.[1]

Creation stories

The Genesis account of creation is one part of the whole biblical story, which deals with the nature and revelation of God, and his relation to his world and to human beings. The biblical story differs from other ancient creation stories in its assertion of the sovereignty and transcendence of God, and in the special place it gives to humanity. Creation by a sovereign God is, indeed, an important doctrine throughout the rest of Scripture outside the first chapter of Genesis. In the Psalms Yahweh is celebrated as the creator, over and against other gods.[2] He is the Lord of the whole created order, as presented in Job 38—41. Deutero-Isaiah ties the whole of creation together – past, present, future, and new creation.[3] In the New Testament we find Christ defined as the agent of creation.[4] When we combine these passages with others that speak of the presence of the Spirit of God in creation, in the individual life, and within the gathered community in re-creation, we find a Trinitarian character to creation as witnessed to in the whole scope of the Bible. But, for all this, there is a special contribution made by Genesis 1; it firmly locates human life within cosmic history, as part of God's purpose. This emphasis gives significance to human life in relation both to God and to the world. But the world in which the Bible took shape was full of stories about creation.

One of the first questions that even the most primitive society probably would ask is, 'How did this world come about?' It is probable that all people groups question the origin and meaning of life, and we find that many of them have developed their own stories of creation. For example, according to a Chinese account of creation there was a huge egg called Chaos.[5] Inside the egg there slept a god called Pan Ku, who held a hammer in his right hand and a chisel in his left (the first geologist no doubt!). Pan Ku lived for 18,000 years and grew nine kilometres in height each day (60 million kilometres in total). Then he died – a very tall person! After his death, his body formed the Earth, his head the mountains, his breath the winds, his voice the thunder, his bones the rocks, his teeth the precious stones, his blood the seas, his hair the trees, his sweat the rain, and the insects on his body were human beings. At this point the Emperor of the world sent time and light into being. He achieved this by standing on the highest mountain with the sun in his left hand and the moon in his right.

Another early tradition on origins arose in India around 2000 BC and was codified in the *Rig-veda* (c.1200 BC). According to this tradition, in the beginning there was the One, who breathed by its own energy. Then desire entered the One and Thought was created. From that came light, and then all the rest.

According to the Greek writer Hesiod (c.750 BC), the beginning of the world is chaos, together with the divine beings of Gaia, Tartarus, and Eros. Next is the birth of the Titans, followed by various disputes and the birth of the gods. The twelve major gods make their home on Mount Olympus, from where this pantheon rules the world. Geologist Cesare Emiliani comments on Genesis 1 that 'as one can see, the Jews make the world very simply, in six days and in (almost) logical order. The story makes rather good sense.'[6] But then he goes on to reflect upon the Greek creation story: 'one must admit that this story is much more interesting than that chronicled in the Bible. At the end of creation, the Jews still had the same old god, but the Greeks had 12 major gods to choose from, plus a vast number of minor ones.'[7] We will remember the apostle Paul's reflection upon this in his meeting with the philosophers at Athens, recorded in Acts 17.

The flood is also a primeval story and belongs to myths of the beginning, and as such relates to the story of creation. It is generally agreed that such stories of world catastrophe are the mythological complement of creation stories. This connexion is not limited to the myths of the ancient Near East, but is found in other primitive stories from around the world, for example in the Benua-Jakun tribe on the Malaysian peninsula, and the Shawnee Indians of North America.

We therefore find that the Genesis accounts of creation, and the other passages in the Old Testament that are concerned with creation, are not unique. There are many accounts of creation from other peoples, but in particular parallels are found with stories of creation and flood in Babylonian, Canaanite, and Egyptian mythology. Recognition of such parallels might lead us to ask whether Genesis presents us with a similar picture of creation or whether it represents something different. I maintain that the Bible presents us with accounts of creation which are both of theological importance, and perceptive of the observable world in which they are written. But first we will need to consider their relationships with creation stories preserved by Israel's neighbours.

The creation accounts of the surrounding nations had to be modified to suit the originality of the Yahwist faith. Neighbouring peoples held that the universe was composed of three levels: of sky, earth, and subterranean abyss or water. The stages of development of the universe were: division/ separation; the edifice constructed; then the heavens and the earth are peopled. In the cosmogonies of the Near East, chaos precedes cosmos; the gods of order destroy the gods of disorder. 'The dominion of the ordering gods over original reality – both divine and amorphous, monstrous and threatening – can never be complete and consolidated. It must submit to a recurring cycle. The purpose of human beings is to assist the victorious gods in that cycle,' hence the new year rituals and the role of the king.[8]

Babylonian, Canaanite, and Egyptian stories of creation

It is possible to recognize similarities within these ancient stories, and suggestions are made of groups of people borrowing from each other. However, with the fragmentary and incomplete nature of some of the texts it may be safer to say that there was a common background to the stories that have been preserved.

The Egyptians were polytheistic, and although many of their gods were depicted as animals, there was no totemism; these were simply the forms in which the divine power manifested itself. The Egyptians did not imagine their life to be precariously balanced, but orderly and changeless – an order, notes Bright, that was 'established at creation, as regular in its rhythm as the Nile floods. The cornerstone of this unchanging order was the god-king.'[9] The economic stability of Egypt depended on the fertility produced by the flooding of the Nile floodplain and delta. This allowed it to be the 'bread-basket' of the Mediterranean.

While no consistent cosmogony was developed by the Egyptians,

Drane has drawn attention to the worship of just one god, the sun god Aten, by Pharaoh Akhen-aten (1369–1353 BC), at the time of the Israelite presence in Egypt.[10] He notes the resemblances between the worship of Aten and the religion of Moses. Others have noted the similarity of language between Psalm 104 and the hymn to the sun, attributed to Akhen-aten, but urge caution in concluding that the hymn to Aten is the source of the Psalm.[11] Drane notes that there is some suggestion that Akhen-aten's hymn may be based on Canaanite religious poetry, which again points us toward common mythologies.

Canaan, before the Israelite settlement, was controlled by the Egyptians, who were the dominant power bloc in the region. Canaan was of strategic importance to Egypt's security, and each city and its king was responsible to Egypt. The great trade routes ran through Canaan from Egypt to Syria and Mesopotamia, and with the trade must also have come a mixing of myths and rituals. It was along this trade route that Abram followed God's call to leave Mesopotamia and journey to Haran, which ultimately led to the establishment of Israel, as God's chosen people, in Canaan.[12]

The Ugaritic texts present stories of Ba'al and the various Canaanite gods and goddesses, which pre-date Israel and provide part of the religious context for the Old Testament. John Day considers that these texts suggest a Canaanite rather than Babylonian origin for the Old Testament references to Yahweh's conflict with the sea (waters) and dragon (Leviathan and Rahab). The Ugaritic texts contain an account of Ba'al's defeat of the rebellious sea-god Yam, as a result of which he is acclaimed king; and also allusions to the defeat of Leviathan (Lotan or Litan), 'the twisting one', 'the powerful one with seven heads'.[13] But, while such comparisons may be made, Mason notes the parallels between the Ugaritic texts and the Babylonian myths.[14] Ba'al is imprisoned by Yam, the sea god (cf. Tiamat of *Enuma Elish*), but encouraged by the divine craftsman, Kothar-and-Hasis, kills Yam with two clubs and scatters Yam's body. Ashtarte the goddess proclaims Ba'al's victory and a temple is built for Ba'al and Kothar-and-Hasis. The texts also contain struggles between Ba'al and Mot (death), and Ba'al and Lotan (the giant sea-monster).

The Babylonian epic *Enuma Elish*[15] may well have influenced the author of Genesis. It represents the success of the hero-god Marduk. It begins with the earliest generation of gods and leads up to the hero-god, through whom the forces of evil are overcome and the order of the universe is established. In the beginning there was no heaven, earth, land or sea, only the gods. There were the gods Apsu and Tiamat who had children and grandchildren. Apsu and Tiamat planned the destruction of the other gods, but learning of their plan the water god Ea fought against Apsu and killed him and made a home from his body. Angered by his death, Tiamat planned revenge. She made poisonous creatures and another god, called Qingu, whom she appointed the commander of her army. Realizing the danger, the gods asked who would fight on their behalf. 'Who rushes into battle: Marduk the Hero!' (Tablet II). Marduk struck up a deal for his involvement: 'Whatever I create shall never be altered! Let a decree from my lips never be revoked, never changed!' (Tablet III). Marduk was victorious and killed Tiamat, Qingu, and all the poisonous creatures, and was made king. As part of the ordering of creation Marduk cut Tiamat's body in half, forming the sky from one half and the earth from the other. Marduk made up his mind to perform miracles and with Tiamat's blood he made human beings (Tablet VI), who were to be always subservient to the gods. The epic ends with a celebration of praise to Marduk, the Lord of creation: 'With fifty epithets the great gods called his fifty names, making his way supreme' (Tablet VII).

In presenting his thesis for an essentially Canaanite influence, Day concedes that the text containing the myth of Ba'al's defeat of Yam makes no reference to the creation of the world. But then, in what appears to be a circular argument, he suggests that because the Old Testament links the image of conflict of the dragon and the sea with the creation of the world, the Canaanites also made this connection.[16] He maintains that the Canaanites may have associated creation with the conflict with the dragon, Leviathan, which occurs at the end of the Ba'al cycle, which describes the first New Year.

Neither Egyptian nor Ugaritic literature contains an account of a great flood, but in Babylonian literature there are a number, the most complete being the Epic of Gilgamesh. This story tells how Ut-napishtim is warned by the god Ea that the other gods, led by Enlil the storm god, had decided to send a flood. Ut-napishtim builds a boat (a cube), and fills it with family, belongings, animals and skilled craftworkers. There is a great storm and flood, the boat runs aground on a mountain when the storm has ceased; a dove, a swallow, and a raven are sent out. Ut-napishtim leaves the boat and offers a sacrifice to the gods, around which they all crowd to savour the aroma. The gods promise that there will be no more floods and give immortality to Ut-napishtim and his wife. Another account, the Atrahasis epic, explains the flood as the gods' decision to rid the world of men and women because they were making too much noise.

Where the stories interact

There is clearly a common stock of mythical material in the ancient Near East, although known in different forms. John Bright rightly points out that it is logical to assume that the traditions which lie behind the creation narratives in Genesis were brought from Mesopotamia by migrating groups in the first half of the second millennium. He supports this with the evidence that a fragment of the Gilgamesh Epic was found in fourteenth-century Megiddo.[17] We can also see that the stories of the Garden of Eden, Genesis 2—3, and Tower of Babel, Genesis 11, have a clear Mesopotamian background. Wenham suggests that Genesis 1—11 comes from a different pre-literary tradition from the patriarchal narratives of Genesis 12—50. The early chapters use and modify stories well diffused throughout the ancient world (such as the Sumerian flood story and Babylonian parallels with the flood story), whereas the patriarchal stories with their focus on the origins of the nations were probably passed down through the Israelite tribes.[18]

Genesis shares much of the thinking of the ancient world of the Near East but presents an alternative worldview, challenging assumptions about the nature of God, the world, and humankind. As we noted in chapter 1, Genesis appears to be a polemic against many of the perceived notions of the gods and the world, and as such does have much in common with ancient thought. While there are aspects in common with, for example, the Atrahasis epic and the Epic of Gilgamesh, the writers of the opening chapters of Genesis need not have read these, as they would have been part of the philosophical culture of their world. There is common agreement that there is an invisible supernatural world, that god(s) were personal and could communicate, and that human beings are both physical and spiritual and are in the image of God. Yet the polemical thrust is clear throughout the creation narratives and beyond. For example, in the accounts of creation, human beings have a central place, rather than being an afterthought – created to supply the gods with food; the flood is the result of sin and not of noisy human neighbours leading the gods to send a flood; Babel is not the centre of Babylonian civilization and the gate to heaven, it is folly. As Wenham concludes, the originality of the writers' message was in affirming the unity of God in the face of polytheism, his justice rather than his caprice, his power as opposed to his impotence, his concern for human beings rather than his exploitation. Whereas Mesopotamia clung to the wisdom of primeval human beings, Genesis records their sinful disobedience, all of which, for the biblical authors, are the central themes.[19]

We know that Israel was influenced by the pagan religions of the nations around them. We can take examples from Josiah's clean-up operation as recorded in 2 Kings 23.1–25. The Canaanite fertility cults of Baal and Ashtarte, the astral cults of Assyria and Babylon, and worship of the sun, moon, and stars of heaven were all in evidence. These all involved a cost of allegiance, but none more extreme than the sacrifice of children to Molech. As the period of settlement in Canaan wore on, the cult of Yahweh had become one among many, and not always the principal one. This helps us to understand the ways in which the biblical writers deal with questions of creation and origins.

The account in Genesis 1, in its historical context, is unique. God, earth and sky are put in relationship; God created sky and earth; God faces chaos, speaks his word, divides, forms, orders, distributes, populates, blesses, and verifies that it is good. As Pedro Trigo concludes, 'only God and creation, God and the divine deed exist'.[20] This leads David Atkinson to state: 'One can imagine what a rock of stability this chapter would have provided for the people of God when faced with the lure of pagan myths around them.'[21] This would certainly apply to Jewish exiles in Babylon, as we discussed in Chapter 1.

This concept of God, from the beginning, is opposed to the myths of the surrounding peoples. The Old Testament shows unmistakable knowledge of the story of conflict between God and the dark waters of chaos, together with the monsters that live within it; some speak of unruly waters threatening to bring chaos;[22] and others speak of monsters emerging from the depths to challenge God's power.[23]

Genesis 1—3

Stanley Jaki suggests that whatever similarities there may be in the flood stories, the creation story of Genesis 1 is far removed from its alleged Babylonian counterpart. 'In *Enuma elish*, the creator-god Marduk is a Johnny-come-lately in a vast crowd of gods, whereas in Genesis 1, God, or Elohim, is the sole agent from the very start.'[24] Marduk is picked by the gods as the avenger. The confrontation is so 'gorily bloody as to obliterate any trace of the starting point', which was the opposition of the freshwater god, Apsu, and the salt water god, Tiamat. If familiar with

Enuma elish, the author of Genesis 1 intentionally formulated a very different cosmogenesis that contrasts sharply with its Babylonian counterpart, and has a very different message:

Enuma elish	**Genesis 1**
Many gods	One god
Gods are part of the world	God is not part of the world
Matter exists first	God exists before anything
Gods fashion heaven/earth	God wills creation
Stars play role in creation	Stars are part of God's creation
Sea creatures are rival gods	Creatures created, not rivals[25]

God is the author of the whole world. The creation of human beings may be seen as the focal point of Genesis 1, but not its conclusion, for, of all the days of creation, it is the day that God ceased that is blessed and sanctified.

In the polemic against the myths and religious concepts of the ancient Near East we see that God created the whole universe out of nothing – a rejection of the idea that matter existed before the gods.[26] The sea monsters and the astral bodies are created – they are not rival deities. Human beings are not servants of the gods – they are God's representatives on earth. Finally, the seventh day is not a day of ill omen – it is a day of blessing and sanctification. Wenham recognizes four features that can be emphasized: a) God is without peer or competitor; b) God is more than creator, he is law-giver: light and dark, land and sea, night and day; c) the world reflects its creator, being the perfection of God's will; d) we see the true nature of human beings – in the image of God, in relationship with God, able to subdue the earth.[27]

Genesis 6—9

It is the differences, rather than the parallels, between the Genesis flood story and those of the Gilgamesh Epic and the older Atrahasis epic that shed light on the theological interests of Genesis. It is Yahweh's moral decision to bring a flood because of the evil of human beings who were ruining the earth; this is very different from the majority view of the gods who were annoyed at the noise that humans are making. God is in control of the flood, not fearful of what is unleashed. The closing scene makes the difference clear: sacrifice leads to the reassertion of the creator's lordship over his creatures and his determination to uphold the cosmic order and his mercy towards human beings, rather than the gods crowding around the sacrifice, some surprised that there are any survivors of the flood. Noah is not a king who gains immortality, he is merely a commoner whose obedience is all that matters.[28]

The Flood can be seen as marking the break between proto-history (dealing with the origin of the whole created order) and pre-history (explaining the origin of the peoples of the earth). In stressing this division, Genesis agrees with the Mesopotamian traditions, yet it makes different theological points. The polemical themes of Genesis 1 continue in the Flood story. There is one God who sent the flood, shut Noah and the animals in the ark, remembered Noah, brought him out on dry land, and gave him a guarantee that never again would the earth be destroyed by a flood. The Mesopotamian gods make no such pledge, and by their very argumentative nature would seem incapable of ensuring its fulfilment. God is moral in his dealings. Noah is the one who is blameless, who 'walked with God', whose sacrificial offering underlines his righteousness, and who lives in a covenant relationship with God. The world is given a new start, with a new blessing; creation is redeemed, but all too soon human sin places a question mark over the future.

Psalms

Unlike the Genesis 1 account of creation, Psalm 104 has parallels, according to Jaki, with the Aten (Sun) Hymn composed by Akhenaten IV, although such parallels probably result from a common worldview with Egypt. However, even here there is no suggestion of worship of the Sun.[29] In contrast, Weiser believes that this beautiful poem is a rich picture of the outline found in Genesis 1. He adds that the picture presented bears the influence of the poet's time: it makes use of the contemporary worldview, and there are parallels with Babylonian, Egyptian, and Greek mythology, especially an affinity with the hymn to the Sun composed by Egyptian king Akhenaten.[30] Allen supports this view, recognizing the marked similarities with the hymn to Aten, but also the links with Genesis 1, which he suggests reveal a clear Hebrew cosmology.[31] Rather than conclude that Genesis 1 uses Psalm 104, he suggests that it would be safer to take the view that both texts express the same Israelite theology. If the psalm was part of the hymnody of the cultus, then we can suggest that a later writer, if Genesis 1 is later, would have had his theology shaped by the cultus.[32] Whatever the links or otherwise, this interpretation of the natural world is to be seen as a courageous act of faith, when the nation's experience and the competing religious outlooks might suggest something different.

Psalm 148 is a call for praise in respect of Yahweh's work in creation and control of the heavenly order, together with his intervention for his people's sake. This psalm has parallels with Mesopotamian and Egyptian hymns, and similarities with other creation psalms, such as 8, 19, 29, and 104. Some authors have suggested that the psalm is a version of Genesis 1.1—2.3, with verses 1–6 paralleling Genesis 1.1–19, and verses 7–14 Genesis 1.20—2.3. Allen believes that it is more likely that Genesis 1 was the influence for the hymn writer.[33] The Psalm is usually dated as post-exilic, maybe early fourth century BC. We noted in Chapter 1 its use by the three men in the furnace.[34]

New Testament

In the New Testament we find a background understanding of God the creator. Jesus noted that people saw the signs of order that were provided by creation: Matthew 16.1–4. He declares that God is faithful and his faithful provision is demonstrated by Jesus' agricultural parables.[35] Paul also understood God to be the faithful creator, as seen in his speech recorded in Acts 14.15–17. In his address to the educated élite of Athens, who would have understood the world in the manner of Hesiod's account (see page 13, above), Paul draws attention to the temple to the 'unknown god', in the midst of a street of temples. He proclaims that the unknown God is to be seen in creation's vastness, in the provision and order of the world, and through human beings, whom God has created.[36]

The purpose of myths

There are three main meanings given to 'myth':

1 A story of gods and goddesses, in which they behave as if they were human beings.
2 A technical term for the text of a religious rite, such as the recital of *Enuma Elish*.
3 A story that expresses a deep meaning of human life that could not be presented in terms of science or history. This third meaning is the one that best describes the biblical stories of creation and flood.

Enuma Elish tells how Marduk championed the cause of the other gods in battle with Tiamat, the dragon symbolizing the ocean of chaos. After

Tiamat's body is cut in two by Marduk to form the earth and heaven, the gods have a temple built in Babylon for Marduk, as his reward. Mason helpfully suggests that this literary epic is used for propaganda purposes, to legitimate the temple of Marduk in Babylon and the reign of its priest-kings. The myth formed the written text (*legoumena*) of the religious ritual (*dromena*), which was enacted at the time of the annual New Year festival. Mason indicates that this was designed to

> 'renew' the primeval victory of Marduk over the forces of chaos, so that regular rainfall would again make possible the annual fertility of the land.[37]

The king plays the central role in the ritual, so that the religion maintains order in the kingdom. Similarly, when discussing the Ugaritic stories of struggles between Ba'al, Mot and Lotan, Mason concludes that

> the whole cycle seems linked with the renewal of the seasons, with the 'death' of vegetation during hot, arid summers and the renewal of life with the coming of the rains. The victory of Ba'al by which he is re-established as king is a guarantee of the renewal of 'order' and 'fertility'.[38]

When we consider the biblical accounts we recognize clear differences. These are first and foremost in their view of God, for whereas Israel's covenant-God makes himself known in personal and moral action, and can therefore be experienced as spiritual personality independent of nature, the Babylonian and Canaanite conceptions of God remain rooted in nature myths where natural forces are personified, the gods emerging along with the rest of matter. Events are cyclical, with the stars determining events. Although Israel shared a cyclical pattern with regard to seasons, New Year, and enthronement, she also conceived a purposeful process in time, with creation as the beginning of her purposeful history. The Old Testament, like the New Testament, presents us with the freedom and sovereignty of God with regard to the world, but at the same time presents the intimate connection between the world and God.

Unlike the gods of other ancient Near Eastern stories, Yahweh is not identified with nature; he is above it and beyond it, yet at the same time is directly involved in the work of creation.[39] Westermann states that the link with existing traditions is important, unless the Yahwist (J) and Priestly (P) writers simply wished to state that Israel's saviour was the creator of the world. The creation stories look back to the tradition that is received, and forward to the history of Israel as the people of God. The primeval story links Israel with the history of the nations. In the transition from Genesis 11 to Genesis 12 we see that the primeval story is the prologue to the history of God acting with Israel.[40] The stories as told by J and P are adapted to convey what they wanted to communicate to the people of their time. The primeval story is linked to the nation's history, which frees creation from the realm of myth and gives it the resemblance of history. This is made clear in Deutero-Isaiah and Job, where in distress or despair the people look to the creator, and in him find the God who saves.

In similar vein, Weiser says that the psalms go back to an early date in Israel's history and were a part of the celebration of the covenant. Whereas the other Near Eastern religions performed a myth that was the destiny of the god, 'the heart of the Old Testament hymn is the *self-revelation* of Yahweh in his theophany.'[41] For the people of Israel, unlike their neighbours, the hymns of praise are a part of their salvation history, which was their living experience. The praise of Yahweh as creator is related to his people's experience of his saving deeds. Creation as the work of the creator was seen through their experience of the covenant: the God of Abraham, Isaac, and Jacob was also the creator of heaven and earth. The theme of creation is tied up with salvation history; Yahweh is Lord of history. Borrowing from the creation myths of other religions links nature with history, demythologized or historicized and used in a metaphorical sense depicting Yahweh's victory over the powers of chaos. Day warns that while the images of the myths were demythologized and historicized for some, those who practised a syncretistic form of Yahwism, equating Yahweh with Ba'al[42] and worshipping the host of heaven,[43] would have seen the divine conflict with the dragon and the sea as living. For the others, Israelite monotheism would have transformed the myth out of all recognition.[44]

In the thinking of the other nations the waters of chaos were personifications of the natural forces that appeared to bring productive life to a standstill at the end of each season. But in the Old Testament this imagery is either clearly placed in the context of God's control over nature, or it is used to support the great events of Israel's history, for example the crossing of the Red Sea, which allowed the people's escape from Egypt.[45] The monsters are seen to be the symbols of Israel's enemies. Statements about Yahweh defeating the chaos monster Rahab or Leviathan are simply used to demonstrate Yahweh's power to rescue his people. Drane is right to point out that the imagery of the myth is separated from its context and given new meaning within the proclamation of Israel's faith.[46]

Significance

The important question that will underlie our reflection is, what sort of God do we believe in? There are a variety of myths in ancient cultures, some of which deny nature and some of which emphasize its importance in the scheme of things. When we look at the Genesis accounts of creation we need to recognize the land in which Israel grew, where there was a need of constant toil in digging irrigation ditches, planting vineyards, and rotating crops and pasture, to keep the wilderness or chaos in check. Israel grew up amongst peoples who saw the divine revealed in nature, in the rhythms of the natural world, especially fertility and sexuality. Any trust placed in the Canaanite gods by the Israelites was attacked by the prophets of Yahweh. Israel's God was revealed in concrete historic events; he was the God who liberates, the God of the exodus, though also the faithful God of the seasons. Through liberation they were brought to a land of promise, where they celebrated the Covenant and the Passover. They assumed the reality and activity of God, who had revealed himself to Abraham and Moses, and who is the Lord and sole creator of the universe.

There are universalist and exclusive trends in Israel's presentation of God – an exclusivity that saw Yahweh worshipped in the temple at Jerusalem; and a more universalist view that saw God as trans-national, incorporating other nations and religions. Clements suggests that one striking characteristic of Yahweh is that he possesses personality. The avoidance of any hint of female sexuality may be accounted for by the wish to distance Yahweh from the female goddesses of the pagan cults. Yet God is not identified as masculine either, as we see in Ezekiel's attack on those who would use male images in worship;[47] any sexuality is to be eschewed. Animal images are also to be avoided.[48]

Israel is called to the exclusive worship of Yahweh, with a separation from the sexuality and images of the pagan deities. Yahweh is Israel's God and is not identified with the gods of other nations. Yahweh is superior to the gods of Egypt[49] and Babylon.[50]

There is a strong polemic against the astral religion of other nations. Trigo helpfully draws attention to the central position of the disproportionately long section in Genesis 1 dealing with the sun, moon, and stars, those regulators of time.[51] This may indicate the tremendous force of the belief to which the Genesis account is opposed, and the danger these astral religious beliefs posed to the faith of Israel.[52] There was a malign influence in worshipping the astral powers which influenced all of life. An agricultural people depended, after all, on the cycles of sun, moon, and seasons, which coincided with the appearance and disappearance of stars. Israel, herself, saw the sun, moon, and stars as 'signs and seasons' for the great festivals in her calendar, when God graciously met with his people to renew them. But Trigo is correct in emphasizing that

> the text of Genesis demythologizes everything it possibly can. First it detaches the heavenly bodies from light, relegating them to a more modest, derived function. Second it omits their names, referring to them generically as luminaries. Third, it deprives them of any influence on human destiny. Their role is to light the earth and distinguish day from night.[53]

It is God who made them, yet the feature that expresses the uniqueness of Yahweh most clearly is the prohibition of images. An image could be thought to convey a degree of access and therefore control over the god. Yahweh is seen to possess freedom and transcendence that would be compromised by such an image. It is in the exilic age that the sharpest polemic against images is found, in which the reasons become theological – Isaiah 40.18–20; 44.9–20. You cannot make a god; God is the creator of all things.

Clements believes that the uniqueness of Israel's conception of Yahweh might have led to a narrow, exclusive view of a national god, but for a number of factors that contributed to a wider thinking.

i) Yahweh's role as creator of the material universe. The J account of Genesis 2.4—3.24, dated during Israel's buoyant nationalism, makes an important point – concern with God as creator at this time would have widened the theological horizons of the nation. In the exilic period arguments for Yahweh's uniqueness begin with creation.

ii) In neither J nor P is Israel accorded a special place in creation; 'the Old Testament fully recognises the openness of the entire created order to Yahweh's control . . . that other nations also have their own role to fulfil within creation is fully accepted in the narratives of Genesis 1—11.'[54]

iii) Yahweh is seen to control the nations and their histories, and brings his judgement upon them.

iv) The universal nature of God is seen in the development of morality, spelt out in Micah 6.6–8.

We have recognized the development of the biblical accounts of, and reflections upon, creation in the context of the mythical stories of origins found in the ancient Near East. We have noted the purpose of those myths in establishing order, stability, worship, and monarchy for Israel's neighbours. However, it has become increasingly clear that Israel's own stories of creation are polemical, and have a propaganda role in establishing Yahweh as the one true God of world history and world creation. In demythologizing the stories of their neighbours, Israel historicized creation and linked it with their tradition of development as the people of God, from Abraham onwards.

We are now in a position to consider in detail what the Israelite faith has to say about creation.

3 Creation as an Act of the Covenant God of Biblical Faith

Whenever I bring clouds over the earth and the rainbow appears in the clouds, I will remember my covenant between me and you and all living creatures of every kind.[1]

Introduction

'Our faith is a present experience; but it has biblical roots,' says Pedro Trigo[2] as he begins a dialogue with Genesis 1, which he rightly states 'was composed at a moment of great need, and of national prostration and disenchantment. It represents the victory of a robust faith then – one which could communicate serenity and hope.' But it is also important for our own understanding of faith that we consider creation, for, as Brueggemann says, 'it is the same God who calls the world and who calls the special community (church). Both creations, world and community of faith, spring "fresh from the word"; both have been evoked by the speech of this God.'[3] Genesis has this same interest, shown in the broad division: 1—11 the world; 12—50 a special people. The twin focus is the call and promise of God.

We have already noted that the biblical accounts of creation belong in the context of the mythical stories of beginnings found in other ancient Near Eastern religions. A myth's function is to give justification to that which is essential for human life and society. In our examination of the Ugaritic stories and of *Enuma Elish* we recognized that the primary function of the myth is to maintain the stability of the present state; this is a common feature of the circle of stories about creation or beginnings of the world and of human beings. Such stories are not intellectual inquiries into the origin of the universe, but rather seek to answer the question of existence itself.

Some ancient myths have a creation without divinity; others, like those of the ancient Near East, have a creator god. When Israel spoke of God as creator they shared this belief in common with their neighbours.

But the difference comes in the uniqueness of Israel's creator-god, and in his covenantal relationship with his creation.

The Flood is a story of salvation which presumes the punishment of humanity by means of a flood. The discovery of the Gilgamesh epic shows that the biblical story stands in a well established tradition, which predates it by a thousand years or more.

The presupposition in the flood stories is that the creator god(s) can also make the decision to destroy. This leads Westermann to comment that:

> the complementarity and almost equal distribution in cultures of creation and flood stories means that human consciousness of its own and of the world's state goes hand in hand with a consciousness that there may be a total destruction which transcends both the death of the individual and the annihilation of the cosmos.[4]

The salvation by God and the subsequent covenant with Noah and the whole of creation, that is grounded in the flood story, becomes an important event for the Old Testament religious community.

The creation stories in Genesis 1—3 look back to the tradition that is received and forward to the history of Israel as the people of God. The primeval story links Israel with the history of the nations. In the transition from Genesis 11 to Genesis 12 we see that the primeval story is the prologue to the history of God acting with Israel. As we noted earlier, the stories of creation and flood, as told by J and P, are adapted to convey what they wanted to communicate to the people of their time. This becomes clearer in Deutero-Isaiah and Job, where in distress or despair the people look to the creator, and in him find the God who saves.

Brueggemann notes that there are three ways in which human and non-human creation are treated: undifferentiated, both the same before God, as in Genesis 9.9–10; human beings superior to non-human creation, as in Genesis 1.25–30; 2.15; and anthropocentric, totally human centred with no mention of non-human creation, as in Genesis 11.1–9. He maintains that

> The theologians who work in a distinctively Israelite way in Gen. 1—11 want to affirm at the same time (a) that the ultimate meaning of creation is to be found in the heart and purpose of the creator (cf. 6.5–7; 8.21) and (b) that the world has been positively valued by God for itself. It must (therefore) be valued by the creatures to whom it has been provisionally entrusted (1.31).[5]

We can describe this view of creation as covenantal and affirm that the creator has a purpose and a will for creation, which includes freedom and love; and that creation has freedom to respond to the creator in various ways, which we find to include a mixture of faithful obedience and rebellious self-assertion.

We see in the early chapters the troubled relation of creator with creation and God's enduring resolve to have creation on his terms. Yet even when we move into the history of the special people of Israel, this remains unresolved and the relationship unsettled, and so the message is one of promise.

Before proceeding to an examination of the various biblical texts, there are a number of critical issues for us to consider. Wenham notes that modern literary criticism is more concerned with the final edition than with the breakdown into recognized sources. He is right in saying that literary criticism of Genesis 1—11 tells us what the stories meant to the final editor, whereas source criticism only tells us how these stories were composed.[6] Our understanding is helped by viewing the substantial unity of Genesis 1—11. It seems likely that chapters 1—11 come from a different pre-literary tradition from that of the patriarchal narratives of 12—50. Chapters 1—11 modify stories of creation and flood known throughout the ancient Near East, whereas the patriarchal narratives belong to the traditions of the Israelite tribes.

Of the sources, Brueggemann suggests that the Yahwist (J), who produced Genesis 2—3; 4; 11.1–9 and parts of the Flood narrative, may be a critique of royal autonomy (perhaps Solomonic) and thus a polemic against the rebellious pride of the creature who will not live in relation to the creator but craves autonomy.[7] It would be difficult to prove or disprove a link with Solomon. But Brueggemann is right to recognize J's attack on human pride, which sadly is all too common in Israel's, and all human, history. On the other hand, as suggested earlier, the work of the Priestly writers (P), Genesis 1.1—2.3 and parts of the Flood narrative and genealogies, dated during the exile, deals with the problem of despair and hopelessness.

Today, we can fall into the trap of making assumptions about the world that are very different from those of the second millennium BC, and in consequence focus on points that were unimportant to the biblical authors and ignore those that are fundamental. For example, Genesis 1—11 and the creation psalms share much of the thinking of the ancient world of the Near East but present an alternative worldview, which challenges thinking about the nature of God, the world, and human beings.

As we noted earlier, for the Jewish and Christian faiths creation is not careless, casual or accidental; it is God's intention. Creation embodies an obedient unity.[8] God creates by speaking in ways that finally will be heard; as Brueggemann concludes, 'his word has the authority of suffering compassion.'[9]

Genesis 1.1—2.3

Genesis 1 transcends the myths of its neighbours in its view of God – a concept that Trigo suggests lies in the Priestly writers' meditation on the covenant. 'The doctrine of creation is the most extreme representation of the sovereignty of God as experienced by Israel over the course of its history.'[10] It is an expression of her living awareness of her dependency on nature and God's faithful will, even in times of darkness and despair. Christians find this exemplified in the incarnation and resurrection of Christ. God's relationship to creation is a personal covenant of gracious love.

Genesis 1 is different in literary form from the rest of Genesis and indeed of the Old Testament; it is neither exhortation, parable, prophecy, song, nor a list of the contents of the storecupboard of creation. Jaki believes that the unusually systematic character of Genesis 1 should suggest that it contains a literary device which makes explicit the message that everything is totally dependent upon God.[11]

The Genesis account tells us of God's act; there is no mention of 'how' it was done. Trigo believes that the Priestly writers 'regarded the concept of immediate divine action as an adequate characterization of God's immediacy with respect to creation, and especially, of God's personal concern.'[12] He believes that creation by divine word is added to safeguard God's transcendence – expressed in the verb *bara*, which is only used in conjunction with divine activity.

P is both an innovative theologian and a receiver and transmitter of tradition, and in this he allows voices other than his own to speak. This may be seen in his use of the verbs *'asah* ('to make') and *bara'* ('to create'); while for the most part these are interchangeable, P can make a theological point by shifting from one to the other. The tradition that P uses contained the word *'asah*. Sometimes P places a command of God before this mechanical description of 'making', so that the act is connected with the *creative* word of God. To prevent the misunderstandings that might arise from the use of *'asah* (make) P introduces *bara'* (create) into the important passages: that dealing with the creation of the animal world (Genesis 1.21), and in the description of the creation of human beings (Genesis 1.27). The creation of humanity was particularly important to P, who uses *bara'* three times in verse 27. Bernhardt[13] draws attention to the use of *bara'* in the comprehensive introduction[14] and the conclusion of the whole creation account;[15] all is the creative work of God. While van Wolde[16] notes that in this account of creation both the word 'create' (*bara'*) and the word 'make' (*'asah*) occur seven times, as an indication of wholeness and perfection. The creative beginning is complete.

The overall picture is of God creating a world ruled by space and time that provides living space for human beings. In the first three works of creation God 'separated' and 'named' the light (3–5), firmament (6–8), and the sea-land (9–10). This separation creates the space where people live out their lives. God names those basic elements as the world of humanity, and demonstrates that he is master of the world that he has defined. These three works are followed by 'Let the land produce vegetation . . .', the earth being seen here as the mother of all life. After the three works of separation and naming, life can come forth from it, says Westermann, 'but only if the creative word of God is at its origin'.[17] This is followed by works five to eight, in which God gives a destiny to everything that he makes or creates: the heavenly bodies (14–19), beasts of the water and air (20–23), land beasts (24–25), and human beings (26–31). These are created according to their species.

P relates creation in a way that people in his own culture would understand from their own experience and knowledge. God is seen to bless the animate parts of creation, a blessing which both bestows fertility on them, and makes them a part of history. Westermann rightly concludes that Genesis 1 pictures creation as set in space and time which are first brought into being, and so creation is not brought about by a single sweeping act of God. There is a distinction in the text between the first three works of creation, which form the inanimate world, and the second five works of creation, which define the animate life placed within the world. There is a clear progression in this arrangement, which Westermann sums up as, 'everything that God has created has a destiny; this destiny reaches its goal in humanity, which God created as his counterpart; with human beings creation points the way into history'.[18] This sequence between the two groups of works also throws light on the structure of 'days' in the narrative, and this in turn may have a bearing on the relation between science and the creation story.[19]

Most Old Testament commentators discuss the significance of the seven days that give the structure to this passage. Westermann does not believe that this order was imposed by a tradition that P inherited, but rather that P is seeking to make his own theological statement through the succession of seven days. However, his use of the seven day structure may well reflect proximity to Mesopotamian traditions, as the seven day pattern is indigenous to this region. The rest on the seventh day brings creation to its conclusion. Creation then is to be seen as part of history, as being within the kind of time we know and not some distant unapproachable primeval time. The God of creation is the God of history, and the final goal of creation is what is hinted at in the seventh day, namely the celebration of the holy. Creation is depicted in seven days because it ends with the day of worship, the sabbath; worship of God is the ultimate purpose of creation. P's account is thus to be seen as a chronological unity, ordered and directed toward a God-given goal, beginning with creation and leading to the worship of God which continues throughout history. This narrative, in Brueggemann's opinion, is 'concerned with *God's lordly intent*, not his *technique*.'[20] The Bible does not take a stand on scientific theories about the origin of the world; these are all left open. This passage is a proclamation of faith, which is the confession of creation as God's gracious gift. The relation between creator and creation is characterized by both distance (allowing freedom) and closeness (God's attentiveness). There is a 'letting be' rather than a 'must be'.

Van Wolde and Wenham both draw attention to the correspondence between the opening verse and closing verse of this creation story (that is, if 2.4a is part of this account). Both verses indicate that three components are central in this story: God's creating; the time which extends from beginning to history; and the heaven and the earth. The account of the seventh day stands apart from the framework of the other six days. The terms 'heaven and earth', 'God', 'create' reappear in Genesis 2.4a in reverse order to that in 1.1, and so this inverted echo of the opening verse rounds off the section.[21] With or without the inclusion of 2.4a, we can recognize that creation begins in eternity and ends in worship that will continue in eternity.[22]

We see that the starting point is outside human beings – the primacy lies outside us. The universe is created, the plants spring up, and animals live their own lives. The fact that the first page of the Bible speaks of heaven, earth, sun, moon, stars, plants, trees, birds, fish, and land animals is a sign that God is concerned with these as well as humans. God is the author of the whole world. The description of days 3 to 5, which describe those things that affect human beings more closely, is longer than days 1 and 2, and the description of the creation of human beings is the longest of all. So the creation of human beings is seen as the focal point of Genesis 1, 'but not its conclusion', for of all the days, the day God ceased is the only day that is blessed and sanctified.[23]

Human beings are created *imago Dei*. The image of God is not primarily our ability to be or do anything; rather it refers to the particular relationship in which God places himself with human beings, 'a relationship in which we become God's counterpart, his representative and his glory on the earth'.[24] To this Atkinson adds: human abilities and capacities; sexuality and mutuality, creativity and fruitfulness. We become truly human through relationships of love. There is a time factor in relationships – we are human becomings – we have a history with God.

The Priestly writers close their account with the whole of creation caught up in the divine blessing. We can conclude with Brueggemann that 'God is satisfied that the world he has evoked in love is attuned to his purposes.'[25] God's blessing comes not from the Near Eastern myths but from Israel's faith, and this is the ground of her sanity and survival. Genesis 1 is an exilic/post-exilic dynamic worldview, which reveals God's activity and character, which should not be compared with human creativity. It is the first article of Israel's faith; and it has provided the underpinning of modern science in its assumption of unity and order.

Genesis 2.4–25

This story, from the earth's perspective, is seen as a more intense reflection on the implications of creation for the destiny of humanity. There is the crisis that results in alienation. Dietrich Bonhoeffer observes that in the first account of creation we find 'man-for-God', but here we find 'God-for-man', the Lord living on earth, walking in the garden. This is the fatherly God who is near by. This is the 'God of childlike anthropomorphism' as opposed to the deity of Genesis 1.[26] In Genesis 2 God is the subject and the human being is the object. When we reach Genesis 3 the narrative describes something happening between God and his human creatures; man and woman are the subject. But the importance of seeing these stories as a whole, says Westermann, is that 'the purpose of the narrative is to lead to a new understanding of the creation of humanity. God's creature is humankind only in community, only when human beings interact with each other.'[27]

The focus is not cosmic but is on earth; God creates humans with his own hands – a closeness to God, and a definite relationship of creature to creator. The life-giving Spirit of God marks human beings out as different. So Bonhoeffer says: 'The human body is distinguished from all non-human bodies by being the existence-form of God's Spirit on earth, as it is wholly undifferentiated from all other life by being of this earth.'[28]

God shapes Adam from the ground, as a potter or an artist. This shows the bodily closeness of the creator to his creature. We recognize that human life is embodied life, and what we do with our body is not unimportant.

Mason notes that the Hebrew word used for fashioning pottery is *yasar*, which is also used meaning to devise or conceive an idea or project. But then the real skill is in bringing what is conceived into actuality. The wonder and praise of God is not only his wonderful designs, but that he brings them to fruition. Israel's celebration moves from the creator of the universe to the creator of human beings and then to the Lord of history, who is working his purposes out. Genesis 2.7 uses the word *yasar* – God, working like the potter, formed Adam from the clay of the ground: *'adam* from *'adamah*. 'The two are related, and it was by the power and skill of the divine Craftsman that the one was formed from the other.'[29] It is the breath of God which brings him to life. So we have witness to the ambivalent nature of human beings, earthly yet with elements of the divine. Mason notes, 'this thought excited the praise of the Psalmist as he contemplated the wonder of God's "craftsmanship" ... Psalm 8.3–6.'[30] The craftsman also has a sense of pride, a sense of fulfilment, care, love, and, negatively, frustration and anger. We recognize this as we remember that God's relation to his creation is two-way, like parent and child.[31]

God places human beings in his park to cultivate and protect, to be his keeper/estate manager, and in this creativity we find fulfilment. Human beings have a capacity for creativity, as part of being made in the image of the creator. Such creativity is to be understood in God's terms (the Servant Songs and the Cross of Christ), a theme that we will return to in Chapter 8, when we will consider environmental aspects of creation, and explore a theology for earthkeeping.

The description 'the Lord God', used nowhere else in Genesis, combines *yhwh* and *elohim*: sovereign creator of the universe (God) and the intimate God of relationship with humans (Yahweh, Israel's covenant-God). The human being, set in the garden, moulded out of the dust, owing life to the inbreathing of God; yet there is also God's loving concern in providing companionship.

Genesis 2—3 also offers a paradigm of sin, a model of what happens whenever human beings disobey God. It is paradigmatic in that it explains through a story what constitutes sin and what sin's consequences are. Wenham notes that the consequences of human actions are both physical – toil, pain, and death – and spiritual – alienation from God.[32] This model of sin is seen throughout the covenant theology of the Old Testament, as we will see in the section below.

But our concern is not finally the danger of sex, the origin of evil, the appearance of death, or the power of the fall. It is, rather, the summons of God for us to be his creatures, to live in his world on his terms. This leads Brueggemann to identify two agendas in the story: a near agenda, the relation between the man and the woman, which was not likely to have been in the narrator's mind; and the far agenda, that of the narrator, which is how to live with creation in God's world on God's terms. It asks whether there are boundaries before which we should bow; it points out that knowledge gives freedom to act and the capacity to control; it probes autonomy for life, without reference to limit and prohibition. Human autonomy leads to alienation and death for self and for others. Our freedom and vocation to manage creation are set in the context of the prohibition of God.[33]

God's intention was for mutuality and equality in relationships, but now we find human life marked by control and distortion, and permeated by distrust. The near and far, horizontal and vertical, agendas come together in the two commands of love for neighbour and love for God, given by Jesus, as recorded in Matthew 22.36–40.

Genesis 6—9

In Genesis 1 we see God bringing order out of chaos, separating the waters to make space for life; in Genesis 2 we see the creation of a context for life and civilization, and the social context for personal love; Genesis 8—9 shows God's recreative power to make a new world out of a broken one.

Wenham notes the inversion of the number of days (7; 7; 40; 150; 150; 40; 7; 7) and the palistrophe or extended chiasmus pattern of the flood narrative.[34] He draws attention to the parallel of the opening and closing scenes. Both are lengthy divine monologues, addressed to Noah and preceded by God's evaluation of Noah's character and that of humankind. The violence in creation and God's resolve to destroy is paralleled by God's resolve to preserve and make a covenant. Genesis brings out fully the correspondences and contrasts between creation and the flood: the long list of animals, the waters of the deep and the waters of heaven coming together again, the sea enclosing the land. Van Wolde notes the seven days that mark the beginning and end of the flood, which 'confirms the impression that the text refers back to the seven days in Gen. 1.'[35] Wenham helpfully records that one interpretation of the chronology places the destruction of the flood from Sunday to Friday, so that de-creation parallels creation. Van Wolde also recognizes that this is an anti-creation story; God looked at the earth and it was no longer good, so God resolves to sweep away what he has made. The waters are no longer divided, chaos returns, and everything disappears under a mass of water, and the animals (innocent) are destroyed along with the human beings. The word for earth, *erets*, occurs eight times and is central to God's concern.[36] The creator is confronted by people who are destroying the earth. But in the midst of the awful silence of destruction the whole drama consists of a story about salvation – God's preservation of humankind through the one he chooses. The divine wind blows back the waters, echoing Genesis 1.1–2. Then comes the repeat commission to Noah, as to Adam. Noah is to be seen as father of a new humanity just as Adam was head of the old order.

The situation that confronts us is one in which we see that human beings are not good, their continued existence is open to question, the creation decision can be revoked. Brueggemann suggests that the task before us involves not historical data but the strange things which happen in the heart of God that decisively affect God's creation. This is not a story which acts as a vehicle of universal truth, it is a peculiarly Israelite statement in the categories of covenant, about God and his peculiar way of transforming the world.[37]

Van Wolde draws our attention to the use of *yhwh* and *elohim* in this story (cf. discussion of Genesis 1 and 2, page 34 above). *Elohim* is used of God standing by himself, independent of the created world, bringing destruction to the whole created order. *Yhwh* is God of human beings, who is in contact with the creatures and gives them meaning. It is *yhwh* who regrets and feels pain, as he looks on creation and human beings who he is about to destroy.[38] 'God saw that it was good . . .',[39] but now it is wickedness and violence; and the judgement is death. There has been a breach of just order, and a failure to live within God-given bounds. God resolves to destroy creation which has refused to be his faithful obedient creation. This narrative can be compared with the normal prophetic speech of judgement. But the picture is not of a tyrant but of a grieving parent; here is a picture of the suffering and grieving God, but one who is gracious, and with whom Noah found favour. Can God bring the world to an end? asks Brueggemann. Can God change his mind and abandon the world which he so joyously created? Yes. But he can also rescue that which he has condemned.[40] The Flood sets the pattern of creation in reverse.

God's creative power in Genesis 1 is invitational rather than coercive. Noah, in this narrative where human rebellion is writ large, is the bearer of an alternative possibility: he walks with God; he is the model of faith; he is responsive and lets God be God, and in so doing he is the emergence of new humanity. The turning point of the narrative comes in 8.1, where after violence, judgement, and a rising flood, God remembers Noah; the flood recedes, and God makes a covenant with Noah and creation. God remembered Noah and all the animals that were with him in the ark. The waters of chaos cannot cut off God's commitment to his creation, and Noah and every living creature become part of creation restored. Life is to be lived in covenant with God in a renewed creation. The winds blow, the land appears, the birds and animals are set free, and God establishes his personal communion with human beings made in his image.

Noah's response is to build an altar and offer a sacrifice. God is pleased and makes his covenant with the whole of creation: seedtime and harvest, summer and winter, are to be kept in being by God. We see God's grace and patience. God invites his creation to live in covenant with him. The creation blessing and command to be fruitful is repeated – God gives his mandate for creation into the hands of potential evil doers – having spoiled it once, human beings are given responsibility once more.[41]

The covenant is given to all human beings without distinction – it is a community responsibility. God calls every living creature into the covenant of his restored creation, but then decrees the conditions. Human beings live with the tension of a fallen world: animals are eaten for food; there is capital punishment for murder. The sanctity of life is underlined. Even when animals are slaughtered, humans are to recognize that all life is God's property. God is the Lord of life, and there is a prohibition on shedding innocent human life.

God resolves to stay with, endure, and sustain his creation. The flood has not changed human beings but it has affected God's relationship with creation; he is committed to his creation with unlimited patience. But this commitment is costly and painful. The covenant includes not only human beings but the whole of creation. God says 'never again' – a revolution in the heart of God which means that his relationship with creation is now based in unqualified grace. The first creation ended with the Sabbath rest; the recreation ends with the rainbow. God has rested his weapon of punishment. The rainbow is God's never-failing steadfast love. The covenant points back to creation. Atkinson's description is both helpful and almost lyrical:

> This colourful imprint in the heavens of God's purposes and love, points us back to the order and patterns of creation. The rainbow in its vivid splendour indicates to us a *natural* order, which depends on the physics of light and refraction.[42]

But it is also a signal of transcendence pointing to God's creation and covenant. We have moved in the story from judgement to assurance, from destructive anger to promissory vow, from law suit to salvation oracle. The flood must be seen, says Westermann, in the context of the whole of the Old Testament, or indeed, Bible.

> It is the same God who resolves to destroy humankind in primeval time and then to preserve it as long as the earth lasts, who announces (Isaiah 65) destruction to his people at the climax of its history and preserves it in a remnant, who at the last judgement at the end of human history is the judge and saviour of humanity.[43]

We can conclude with van Wolde that a survey of the creation story of Genesis 1—11 represents an account of the creation of the cosmos, about the earth and its ongoing existence, and about human beings on this earth. Although the story is marked by times of progress and setback, development and destruction, in the end God resolves on a covenant with all living beings on earth. In it God guarantees that the earth shall continue to exist.[44] This message through the prophets, especially Deutero-Isaiah, points us forward to the work of Jesus Christ.

Psalms

In its worship, Israel celebrated in song its faith in who Yahweh was and how he related to Israel as his people and to the world which he created.

Israel celebrated God's activity in the world and his mighty deeds, by which he had rescued them from slavery in Egypt. It was this God who was with them in good times and bad. Weiser and Day both place the psalms that specifically deal with creation (namely 8, 19, 65, 104 and 148) in the hymn category. These psalms begin with a call to praise Yahweh, followed by praise of God's attributes, his nature and providential rule. Weiser believes that the hymn goes back to an early date in Israel's history and was a part of the celebration of the covenant. Day would place the writing of Psalm 148 in the post-exilic period.[45] The name of Yahweh is often glorified in the hymn (for example 8.1, 9; 148.13). The name is both revelation and also the affirmation of the people in their faithfulness to God. For the people of Israel, unlike their neighbours, the hymns of praise are a part of their salvation history, which was their living experience. In the Psalms the motif of praising God as creator is almost as common as the recognition that he is saviour of his people.[46]

Weiser maintains that 'as an independent theme of the hymn the idea of creation is to be found only in Psalms 19 and 104, and both of them are hymns which seem to have modelled their subject-matter after foreign patterns.'[47] Weiser suggests that the close links between the psalms and the cult of the Covenant Festival would suggest that they largely date to the pre-exilic period.

Psalm 104

We have already noted the influence of the mythologies of the psalmist's context and the parallels between this psalm and Genesis 1.[48] As part of the corporate worship of Israel, it has been suggested that its setting was in the dedication of Solomon's temple, used in an apologetic role to stress Yahweh's transcendence, especially in respect to the sun-god of Mesopotamian worship.[49] Day has also noted connection with Ugaritic texts, for example the use of the word translated 'the deep' in verse 6.[50] This is a beautiful hymn of praise to Yahweh's power and loving care, to which the world around bears witness. In contrast to other mythologies, the one religious idea here is that God has created the heavens for his own sake, that they might serve his will, witness to his power and wisdom, and reveal his glory.

Yahweh is portrayed as both creator and sustainer of his world. So water, the potential enemy of terrestrial life, has been harnessed for sustenance, producing springs, rivers, and rain. This is a step from chaos to cosmos, where God's care and control are clearly shown. With the help of the waters God establishes life on earth – plants, which provide food and habitation. The whole of nature reveals the wisdom of the creator in the ordering of the universe.

Human beings are at the centre of the psalmist's concern, but they do not stand alone; they share the world with all the other creatures; all are part of God's plan, as we see in Job 38—41, discussed below. The work of human beings is ordained by God[51] and the sun and moon are subordinate; they are Yahweh's clock and calendar for his animate creation.[52] God is sole creator and sole sustainer; his breath is the source of life.[53]

But there is, notes Weiser,[54] a serious conclusion (31—35); it is all for God's glory. God's awesome majesty[55] should pose a warning for the wicked.

Psalm 148

The whole world is called upon to give praise to the creator and preserver of all life. It is the creator who gives meaning to, and who unites, the inanimate created things and the living creatures in a mutual relationship of praise. So Allen[56] is able to speak of a 'Universal Choir' as an expression of the praiseworthiness of Yahweh; the totality of praise from all of creation is itemized. The heavens and their inhabitants are urged to join the universal choir. The call is to praise Yahweh for their creation and preservation, and their endowment with specific roles; and they proclaim his handiwork.[57] Finally the psalmist turns to humankind, especially the rulers of the world nations and all members of the cult community. Belief in the sovereignty of God and in his assurance of salvation is, states Weiser, 'the culmination of the whole psalm and is of crucial importance to the whole world,' and points forward to the proclamation of the angel at the first Christmas.[58]

The Psalm is usually dated as post-exilic, maybe early fourth century BC (the reference in verse 14 may support this). Jaki demonstrates that this Psalm, which relates to the whole of creation, can be seen as the best biblical commentary on Genesis 1, in expressing Yahweh as the creator of the universe:

Verse	Focus
1	in the heavens
2	everybody

3–6   everything
7a   on the earth
7b–10   everything
11–12   everybody
13–14   praise the Lord[59]

The biblical worldview has one major advantage over all the other worldviews: it represents an *all* which has a dynamic character, anchored in a fundamental conviction that the *all* rests on God's omnipotence. So this passage which affirms that the *all* which Yahweh is capable of doing far surpasses all human conception, affirms Israel's faith in the creator as it is recited. There is reason enough to praise Yahweh through the revelation of his majesty in creation, but far more through his re-establishment of the covenant community after exile. They have been restored and can celebrate their relationship with him.[60]

Job 38—41

We live between the beginning and the end with no knowledge of either. The Bible begins with God's willing of creation. But can we trust this word – we were not there at the beginning (Job 38.4). 'In the beginning God . . .' is true if he is present with us in the midst of life with his word, and not only as creator, remote from us. Into Job's situation of suffering God speaks out of the storm.[61] The one who speaks is Yahweh, the covenant God.[62] All through the book of Job God has been referred to as *El Shaddai*, God the Almighty, giving a sense of distance, detachment, and impersonal almighty power. But now as God speaks it is as the Lord of the covenant promise to Abraham; the God of personal care, steadfast love, and faithfulness to the people of his covenant. God had not abandoned Job, his presence is seen in his creation. The Covenant God is the God of creation. God's questions can be seen as educative rather than harsh and threatening. 'It is as though the Lord God is taking a walk through his creation – a walk through the Garden, perhaps, as the storm becomes still – and is inviting Job to accompany him: Do you see this. . . ? Do you recognise that. . . ? As Jesus later invited his disciples to "consider the lilies", so here God is inviting Job to consider the beauty and order and wonder of the created world.'[63] Or perhaps a better comparison with Jesus would be his questions to his anxious disciples after the miracles of feeding.[64] Gustavo Gutierrez comments that

God's speeches are a forceful rejection of a purely anthropocentric view of creation. Not everything that exists was made to be directly useful to human beings; therefore they may not judge everything from their point of view. The world of nature expresses the freedom and delight of God in creating.[65]

We, too, need to be led, by God, to break out of our anthropocentric captivity. The portrayal of creation in these final chapters of Job is reminiscent of Genesis 1, not only in its similar catalogue of the regions of the cosmos and their inhabitants, but also in its alternations of light and darkness. Gerald Janzen observes that no attention to humankind is given in this thorough presentation. 'As a corollary to this absence, all the creatures which are presented are wild creatures untamed by human intervention.' Yet Janzen rightly observes that humankind is there in the shape of Job: 'humankind is that part of creation whom God addresses with questions concerning the rest of creation' – here again are the two dimensions of the divine image: creature and yet addressee.[66] There is a reaffirmation of the nature of creativity and creatureliness, but also a deeper understanding of humankind as divine image. There is a parallel between Job and Genesis. In Genesis 2—3 and Job 1—2 the snake and satan subvert the claims of Yahweh. In Job 38—41 the genuine questions of Yahweh emerge 'when the ironic subversion is recognised.'[67]

From the beginning God creates the sky, sea, light and darkness, the stars and the weather. Job is invited to marvel at the wonder, pattern, and purpose of creation. All life has its place in God's ordering and care. Job must find himself within the whole of creation.[68] Human beings belong, enjoying the creator's handiwork. Divine wisdom is greater than human understanding, and at the end Job realizes his lack of understanding and has nothing left to say. Atkinson concludes that there is a difference between the God of the philosophers and the God who makes himself known. Job's friends' understanding of God was a belief in the workings of natural causes, the logic of reward and punishment, a sterile faith in a God who was far removed, *El Shaddai*, rather than *Yahweh* of the covenant. God is known as revealed through Jesus Christ, who is the covenant God of creation, Abraham, Isaac, Jacob, Moses, and of the New Covenant in Christ.[69] He maintains that wisdom, power and justice describe the God in whose hands all the mystery of this world is held, including suffering. This God is not merely the end of a philosophical or logical argument – his ways and thoughts are higher than ours.[70]

Atkinson rightly notes that we live in a culture that needs rational answers and in a church culture that wants certainties. 'The book of Job, instead, brings us face to face with the living God, and invites us to live in his light with all our logical gaps, untidy edges and struggling faith.'[71]

We shall return to discuss the nature of both revelation and suffering in later chapters, especially in Chapters 6 and 7.

Some New Testament reflections

The Jews of the New Testament period shared the beliefs in creation that we have been discussing so far in this chapter. The passages that speak of creation assume such faith; there is no sense in which the existence of God as creator has to be proved – that part of the creed is taken as read. Thus we see that in the great chapter about faith in Hebrews 11.1–3, the writer begins with his readers' faith in the universe created at God's command.

We see, for example, in Jesus' parables an understanding of the ordering of creation, of the seasons, and of plant growth. Paul demonstrates the same understanding when he compares the growth of the church with the growth of plants.[72]

In debate with the educated élite of Athens (recorded in Acts 17.24f), and in his letter to the church at Rome (Romans 1.20), Paul points to nature as a witness to the creator God.

Luke 12.13–21

Following on from our observations on God's words for Job, the man in Luke's story was a fool because he mixed up working for a living with the meaning of life and creation. There is a need to recognize that the land is God's. Margot Kassmann says that it is

> when a person or a people starts to forget these connections between
> justice and ecology, the consequences can be tragic. Many rich people,
> like Luke's successful farmer, begin to lose their sense of reality. For
> Luke sin is related to exalting oneself; and salvation is not so much
> moral improvement as the liberating insight that it is God's grace and
> being part of the community that will save us.[73]

We can apply this parable to the starvation in one part of the world, while in another they are destroying food mountains. We recognize a clear understanding of the stewardship of creation by human beings, who demonstrate the nature of the creator God. We will consider these issues when we look at a theology for earthkeeping in Chapter 8.

John 1.1–3

John, like the Old Testament writers, contextualizes his message into a community where there were Greek and Jewish influences, and, in similar fashion, proclaims about creation from his community's experience of God, in Christ. He thus interprets the creation of the universe by the word of God.[74]

Renthy Keitzar says that

> what is important here is John's contextualisation. He uses a
> contemporary term, not compromising with his readers'
> understanding, but rather explaining the biblical view of the Word and
> its function through the use of language that can make his theology
> understandable to his readers.[75]

Keitzar recognizes both an evangelistic thrust (Jesus the same as the creator, who gives eternal life to believers) – we become restored, a new creation; and an ecological relevance (the world is created by God and is subject to the control of Jesus).[76] God sends his son to the world because he loves it.[77]

Romans 8.18–23 and Colossians 1.15–20

In Christ there is a new creation but, as ever in the New Testament, there is a 'now but not yet' aspect. There are the first fruits of the Spirit, but still creation groans as it waits for God's human creatures to reach their perfect humanity. To believe in Christ in this world is to believe against reality – Christ is risen, but we live in a world of suffering, pain, and destruction. It is hope, because now we see salvation for all creation appearing only in outline. But this cannot be a cheap hope; human beings must act in hope – the Spirit gives us the possibility to be what we are to become – the children of God.

This same theme is in focus in Colossians 1.15–20; note verses 19–20:

> For God was pleased to have all his fulness dwell in him, and through
> him to reconcile to himself all things, whether things on earth or things
> in heaven, by making peace through his blood, shed on the cross.

44

The whole of creation is brought back into relationship with God through the cross. This takes place as human beings find their restored relationship with the creator, through the cross. God is deeply and passionately involved in his world; he is no absentee landlord, but indwelling, accompanying, incarnate, and present as Holy Spirit. There are important implications for the relationship of human beings both to the creator and to his creation, and we will address these issues more carefully in Chapter 8.

Concluding remarks

The comprehensive statements about creation belong to later texts: Deutero-Isaiah, P, and some psalms, which are difficult to date. This does not mean that Israel before the sixth century did not worship God as creator – the environment of Canaan was saturated with creation myths, and pre-exilic psalms (for example Psalms 19 and 104) demonstrate a belief in God as creator. However, it was probably in this later period that Israel was able to fit creation theologically into her tradition, recognizing the theological connection between creation and her salvation history. It is helpful to have John Day's insights that the conflict with the dragon and the sea, or waters of chaos, have their *Sitz im Leben* in the Autumn Festival, associated with the theme of Yahweh's enthronement as king. Yahweh is thus seen to be Lord of creation and history. Later, Day says, this divine conflict underwent a process of demythologization, and the control of the waters became a 'job of work', as in Genesis 1. The Genesis 1 account he sees as dependent on both Canaanite and Egyptian mythology, as indicated by its close parallels with Psalm 104.[78]

While in Deutero-Isaiah creation is subordinate to salvation,[79] each reference to creation reinforces confidence in Yahweh's power and readiness to save. This soteriological understanding of creation is not confined to Deutero-Isaiah; for example, Psalm 89, celebrating the covenant with David, also includes a section dealing with creation, seen as God's saving acts (5–18). Von Rad believes that this soteriological understanding of creation lies behind the creation stories of J and P, which in turn move on to Abraham and the covenant. This expansion of the credo broadened its theological basis, but this was only possible because creation was regarded as a saving work of Yahweh.[80] Elsewhere von Rad notes the use of the struggle motif between God and chaos, which parallels the Babylonian mythology.[81] This leads him to suggest that 'it is the poets and prophets who unconcernedly and casually make use of these obviously more popular ideas.'[82] Day would, as we have already noted, suggest that these 'popular ideas' were more likely Canaanite in origin.

When we consider the Wisdom literature we find creation, as God's activity, being presented as a basis for faith, as we recognized in our discussion of Job 38—41 above.[83] But this does not necessarily represent a later aspect of theological reflection, as a similar message can be found in Psalm 19.1–6 and Psalm 104.

Only in Genesis 1 and 2, which form the prologue and start of the divine saving work in Israel, are there direct theological statements about creation. Although J uses pictures, von Rad states that he is much more didactic than P, which he sees as moving in the realm of theological definitions. Although J may be dated as a couple of centuries earlier than P, it is unwise to see a development in cosmological thinking. Von Rad maintains that it is not true to describe J as more mythological.

> Assessing the Jahwist according to his intellectual outlook, which is permeated by what are certainly age-old conceptual forms (rivers, a garden, fruit, a tree of life, a serpent), we are met with an enlightened sobriety which uses the old mythological conceptions only as very sublime pictures. In contrast, Gen. 1 presents the results of concentrated theological and cosmological reflexion in a language which is concise and always utterly direct in expression.[84]

In Genesis 1 there is no struggle between gods; creation is the act of God's free will. The world is the product of Yahweh's creative word; it is therefore separated in its nature from God himself, being neither an emanation nor a mythically understood manifestation of the divine. The only continuity between God and his work is his word – cf. John 1.1–5. Human beings are not created by a word, but by the resolve of God himself, and as a result have an immediacy to God.

Yet human beings are not the climax of creation: when God had finished his creating he rested, and all creation joined in the worship of its creator. Here there is no turning away from creation, but rather we find Yahweh turning toward creation as its preserver and sustainer. P is concerned with the 'world' and human beings within it, whereas J shows the construction of our immediate environment and defines our relationship to it. J is more anthropocentric and as such is a supplement to P. God the creator is represented as a potter at work with his clay.

Compared with Genesis 1, the creation of human beings is more personal and a more intimate act of God, yet the life of human beings comes from God's breath, not his own material body. Both accounts agree that human beings have a significant place within God's creation and in relationship with him.

Another significant feature is to be found in the place of the waters of chaos in the creation stories. While in Genesis 1 the waters of chaos are driven back, Genesis 2.4ff. begins with a waterless wilderness, which God transforms. When we reach the story of the Flood we are presented with the return of the waters of chaos, as God's destructive response to human rebellion. When Noah has been saved through the flood, we find the waters of chaos driven back once more and God establishes his renewed covenant with all of creation.[85] The new covenant after the flood reminds us that we are always looking from the side of a broken creation. God's saving of creation is seen in God's heart, as he remembers Noah.[86]

Throughout our examination of these passages we have noted not only the importance of relationship (God with creation; God with human beings; and human beings with God, with each other, and with creation) but also the culmination of this relationship in worship. The climax of creation is worship (Genesis 2.1–3); the climax of the Flood story is worship (Genesis 8.20–22); and the psalms celebrate creation through worship. As we consider the discoveries of science and let the scientists tell their stories of creation, in Part II we will discover aspects of praise, awe, and wonder, as well as the familiar feature of a broken creation, namely human self-centredness. This will lead us forward into renewed discussion of the nature of God's covenant with creation and humanity, in Chapters 8 and 9 of Part III.

4 *Star-gazers Tell Their Stories, Old and New*

Where is the one who has been born king of the Jews? We saw his star in the east and have come to worship him.[1]

How would the 'wise men' tell their story? They spent much time in the study of the stars, no doubt seeking to understand the universe and their existence within it. Their view of the universe would have been similar to that of Aristotle or maybe Aristarchus. A 'new star appeared' – a comet? a nebula? Whatever it was, it led them to Jerusalem and King Herod, and from there to Bethlehem and a very different king. As T. S. Eliot wrote:

> 'A cold coming we had of it,
> . . . were we led all that way for
> Birth or Death? . . .
> We returned to our places, these Kingdoms,
> But no longer at ease here, in the old dispensation,
> With an alien people clutching their gods.[2]

Was it now different? They had followed a star and found a king. The wise men of Jerusalem had quoted a Jewish prophecy about the Messiah of Yahweh, proclaimed in Micah 5.2, and their star had led to a baby or toddler in Bethlehem. Is Eliot right? Could they no longer go back to their myths of creation, maybe of Apsu, Ea, Qingu, and Marduk; or of Aten; or even their science?

And what of the modern star-gazer? Stephen Hawking seeks the 'mind of God',[3] or Paul Davies wonders if we are truly meant to be here.

> What is man that we might be party to such a privilege? I cannot believe that our existence in this universe is a mere quirk of fate, an accident of history, an incidental blip in the great cosmic drama. Our involvement is too intimate . . . We are truly meant to be here.[4]

48

Can they still go back to their agnosticism, or their cosmological equations, and remain unchanged?

The beginnings of science

If the Magi were to tell their story, as wise men who studied the stars, they would speak out of the scientific understanding of their age: Egyptian, Babylonian, and Greek.

As we noted earlier, the Egyptians' view of the universe was dominated by the flood cycle of the Nile, which was essential for their livelihood. They noted that the level of the Nile began to rise with the heliacal appearance of Sirius, the brightest star in the sky in the morning twilight above the eastern horizon. Sothis, as they called it, became the divine star responsible for the Nile's rising, and was identified with the goddess of agriculture and fertility. This cultural environment in Egypt did not lead to a flowering of astronomy.

In Babylonia the stars had been observed as far back as Sargon of Akkad, early in the fourth millennium BC. The major constellations, made known to the Greeks and Romans by Aratus and Eudoxus in the fourth and third centuries BC, had probably been known for over 2,500 years. It was from the Babylonians that the Greeks derived their first notions of astronomy.

The Greeks were, as far as is known, the first people to make detailed observations of the size and structure of the universe. Notable among their scentists were: Thales, who forecast an eclipse of the sun in 585 BC, and improved the art of navigation by the stars; Anaximander (c.610–540 BC), a student of Thales who claimed the earth was free in space, and that the sun, moon, and stars went under the earth to reappear; Pythagoras (c.582–507 BC), who claimed the earth was a sphere (after seeing the curved shadow of the earth on the moon during eclipses), which moved with the sun and other heavenly bodies in circles about a central point; Aristotle, who held to a geocentric model; Aristarchus, who was the first to propose a heliocentric universe; and Hipparchus and Ptolemy, who held to a geocentric system, and produced star charts that lasted for over a thousand years.

Aristotle (384–322 BC) was a member of Plato's Academy. He recognized four causes that produced all things: the full explanation of anything should say what it is made of (material cause), what it essentially is (formal cause), what brought it into being (efficient cause), and what its function or purpose is (final cause).[5] Aristotle's *Physics* sets out a good deal of theory about the workings of the universe, and includes an argument for a Prime Mover, starting from his conception of change and causation. There could be no first moment of change, he argues, as change implies existing matter. There must therefore be an Unmoved Mover, who keeps the heavenly bodies moving and maintains the eternal life of the universe. Aristotle conceived of a universe with a spherical stationary earth at the centre, surrounded by a spherical heaven, on which rotate spherical stars, which are fixed in position.

Aristarchus (310–230 BC) suggested that the sun and the stars remain in fixed positions, while the earth moves around the sun in a circular orbit. His work was largely ignored by his contemporaries, but was known to Copernicus, who some 1,700 years later revived the heliocentric model.

Hipparchus (second century BC) produced a star catalogue of some 850 stars. He sought to measure the distances between the earth and the moon and sun, and made careful measurements of the seasons of the year. Ptolemy (second century AD) built on Hipparchus' star catalogue, and described the solar system in his great work, known by its Arabian name, *Almagest* (c.AD 140). Ptolemy's cosmology explained how sundials work, and the calculation of eclipses. However, in order to keep the earth at the centre of his universe he had to posit eccentric paths for the planets instead of uniform circular motion. In Ptolemy's classification the earth is unique and the planets are wandering stars; the moon and sun are planets; and the rest of the stars are fixed. This model fitted with the Aristotelian physics of his time.

Our knowledge of the solar system has grown more in the last 20 years than the previous 2,000 years. When Newton said, 'If I have seen further, it is because I have stood on the shoulders of giants,'[6] he could have been speaking for almost all who followed in his footsteps during the Enlightenment. George Smoot expresses something of the excitement felt by science when he says:

> As we approach the end of the millennium, cosmology is experiencing a wonderful period of creativity, a golden age in which new observations and new theories are extending our understanding – and awe – of the universe in astonishing ways.[7]

Modern science is building on a long history of discovery. The coming together in the 1970s of studies of the very large (astronomy) and the very small (particle physics) has provided the possibility of answering the ultimate questions. Cosmology claims to be able to look back to 10^{-42}

seconds after what is believed was the Big Bang origin of the universe. But at the moment of creation, the universe probably existed under very different conditions and operated according to different laws than it does today. Smoot concludes that 'reality in cosmology sometimes evades our comprehension'.[8]

It is the scientist who is now posing the questions to which only philosophy or theology has any meaningful answers. Modern cosmologists are posing questions about the beginning and end of the universe, about the place of *Homo sapiens* within it, and the reasons for apparent design and purpose within the evolution of the cosmos. On Christmas Eve 1968, as the first astronauts orbited the moon, Frank Borman read the opening verses of Genesis 1, and all the world was able to hear something of his beliefs. Yet at this juncture we need to stress a point that will be made later, that God's existence is not proved by scientific discovery. Some years before Borman, the first man in space, the Russian astronaut, Yuri Gagarin, declared that he did not find God in the heavens.

Revolutions in science

By 1520 a literal interpretation of Genesis 1 was becoming very difficult. The appearance of the sun on the fourth day was a real problem when it was understood that light came from the sun. The appearance of animal and plant life was also causing difficulty.

By 1650 a new view of the cosmos was appearing. Jaki rightly recognizes that

> all of a sudden Genesis 1 becomes of no concern for those who take the newly-born science for their guide about matters physical. This is not to say that their dicta would thereby become reliable about the origin of the world. But from now on there opens up a gap between Genesis 1 and the genesis of the universe as suggested by science . . .[9]

Paul Thagard observes that

> Scientific knowledge often grows slowly with gradual additions of new laws and concepts. But sometimes science undergoes dramatic conceptual changes when whole systems of concepts and laws are replaced by new ones.[10]

In 1970 Thomas Kuhn noted that the development of scientific knowledge included revolutions, which he described as 'paradigm shifts'.[11] For Thagard a conceptual change is revolutionary if it involves the replacement of a whole system of concepts and rules by a new system. If knowledge of science were neatly accumulative, fact piling on top of fact, there would be no need to speak of revolutions, but he recognizes seven historical cases that can be called revolutionary: i) Copernicus' sun-centred solar system replacing the earth-centred system of Ptolemy; ii) Newtonian mechanics replacing the cosmology of Descartes; iii) Lavoisier's oxygen theory, which replaced the phlogiston theory of Stahl; iv) Darwin's theory of evolution by natural selection, which replaced the divine creation of species; v) Einstein's theory of relativity, which replaced and absorbed Newtonian physics; vi) quantum theory, which replaced and absorbed Newtonian physics; vii) the plate tectonics theory that indicated the earth's dynamic crust, and established the existence of continental drift.[12] Conceptual revolutions require a mechanism that can lead people to abandon an old conceptual system and adopt a new one. This does not take place in a slow evolutionary way; revolutionary thinking and discoveries require a new set of explanatory hypotheses.

These revolutionary changes in thinking did not immediately, nor always in the long term, lead to an abandonment of belief in the Creator-God. Scientists in the late seventeenth century such as Robert Boyle (1627–91) and John Ray (1627–1705) envisaged scientific enquiry as a form of worship. 'The image of nature as temple, the scientist as priest, was explicit in Boyle ... God's craftsmanship in creation could be celebrated by the skilled anatomist.'[13] Boyle spoke of 'pregnant hints' revealed to him from a greater chemist than he. Natural philosophers of the seventeenth century would insist that a doctrine of creation gave coherence to scientific endeavour in as much as it provided a model of an ordered universe, the creation of a rational god. Johannes Kepler (1571–1630) could speak of thinking God's thoughts after him, and René Descartes (1596–1650) could speak of discovering the laws that God had put into nature. In John Ray's *The Wisdom of God Manifested in the Works of Creation* there is a wonder and praise for nature. Ray saw the conceptual revolution of the Copernican system as the elegance one might expect from a divine architect. The process of choosing the simpler theory in science as correct led Michael Faraday in the nineteenth century to 'a God who had ensured that the book of his works would be as simple to comprehend as the book of his words.'[14]

A Polish priest, Nicolaus Copernicus (1473–1543), began to study the movements of the planets in 1513. He suggested that the sun and not the earth was the centre of our solar system, and set out his heliocentric theory in 1543, shortly before his death. Copernicus knew of the work of others such as Aristarchus and Heracleides (a fourth-century pupil of Plato), who suggested that the earth was not stationary but rotated about its own axis, and that Mercury and Venus revolved about the sun like satellites. Copernicus was followed by the Italian Catholic philosopher, Galileo Galilei (1564–1642), who developed a telescope with a magnification of 32, capable of observing the planets. Galileo adopted the Copernican heliocentric theory, observing the mountainous regions of the moon, the stars of the Milky Way, the satellites of Jupiter, the phases of Venus, and sun spots. However, Galileo's publications brought him into conflict with the Catholic Church. Galileo's writings, especially in the area of dynamics, which derived in large part from his studies of ballistics, paved the way for Newton.

Yet before Newton, German astronomer Johannes Kepler (1571–1630) established the law of elliptical orbits of the planets and formulated important truths that applied to gravity, in particular recognizing that the tides on earth could be ascribed to lunar attraction.

Sir Isaac Newton (1642–1727), an English mathematician and physicist, probably contributed more to scientific understanding than any other man or woman, before or since. His laws of motion and gravity made sense of the planetary observations of Kepler, and represent the second of Thagard's conceptual revolutions. Newton's recognition of gravity in 1666 (apples fall off trees, according to the apocryphal story), laid the foundations of a scientific worldview that has dominated western society for 300 years. Newton presented his three laws of motion in 1687 in his magnum opus: *Philosophiae Naturalis Principia Mathematica*. Through Newton's work we have the picture of a dynamic universe, which is never at rest. Newton assumed an equal distribution of stars in an infinite universe. With the stars at an equal distance from each other the gravitational pull is equalized, although the situation envisaged would remain unstable.

For Newton God was not at the centre of the natural process, but outside, holding the whole dynamic system within a timeless and motionless framework. Newton thought of the universe as the rational design of God, with its infinite size related to the all-embracing Spirit of God. For Newton, God was the transcendent creator, the controlling force outside the universe, keeping the boundaries; but such a God could not be on the inside as one of its participants. Newton's work both affirmed God and at the same time limited what he could be and do. The possibility of miracles, revelation, or intervention by God was not possible within a universe governed by natural laws.

Copernicus, Galileo, and Newton together had overturned the entire Aristotelian system. But the move away from a cosy earth-centred universe was not very comforting. Blaise Pascal, the French mathematician (1623–62), expressed the sentiments of many, says Smoot, when he wrote, 'The eternal silence of those infinite spaces strikes me with terror.'[15]

The author of the third conceptual revolution in science, Albert Einstein (1879–1955), had a number of predecessors. Faraday developed the field theory for magnetic forces in the 1840s; Young proposed the wave theory for light; William Thomson, Lord Kelvin, worked in the field of thermodynamics; James Clerk Maxwell in 1861 developed the mathematical theory of electromagnetic fields and assumed electromagnetic radiation; in 1897 J. J. Thompson discovered electrons; and in 1911 Ernest Rutherford recognized the atomic nucleus with electrons in orbit. Max Planck (1858–1947), a German physicist, proposed the quantum theory in 1900, which stated that energy is emitted in packets called photons or quanta. He introduced this theory to explain the distribution of energy across the range of frequencies radiated by hot objects. He showed that the amount of energy in each quantum increased as the wavelength of the radiation became shorter. His theory marks the divide between the classical physics of Newton, Kelvin, and Maxwell, and the modern physics of Einstein.

Einstein established the important principle that the speed of light was always the same, no matter how you measured it. This was the basis of his Special Theory of Relativity. In 1915 Einstein presented his General Theory of Relativity, which demonstrated that gravity is a field like a magnetic field, and is described in the concept of a space-time continuum. This is the combination of 3D space with the fourth dimension of time. Einstein predicted that light bends under the gravitational pull of large astral bodies. One recent commentator on this theory has helpfully likened space-time to a rubber sheet stretched flat. If a heavy object such as a golf ball were to be placed on it the sheet would change shape; there would be a downward curvature in the sheet.[16] This is the way that gravity affects space-time.

Einstein believed in a changeless, uncreated cosmos, with matter evenly distributed. In itself, however, the General Theory of Relativity actually required an expanding universe, as in a static universe the gravitational force would be destructive, causing the whole system to collapse in on itself. Einstein therefore introduced a cosmic constant to counteract the gravitational force. His theory of relativity undermined the Newtonian view of a universe working like a machine, composed of individual parts. Einstein's universe is an interacting whole of space and time. God, for Einstein, was manifested in the laws of nature: impersonal, sublime, beautiful, indifferent to human beings, but still important to them.[17] Einstein affirmed the religious sense of wonder and mystery when looking at creation, but could not accept the idea of a personal God. God was the great unknown and unknowable. Human beings were part of the mystery; he said, 'The most incomprehensible thing about the universe is that it is comprehensible.'[18]

The scientific revolutions of the Enlightenment period have required substantial changes in concepts such as force, gravity, mass, planet, wave, and particle. In the twentieth century, the relativity and quantum theories showed the inapplicability of Newtonian theory to objects that are very massive, very small, or fast moving. The revolutions produced by these theories were more cumulative than other scientific revolutions, but they still involved considerable conceptual change and rejection of previously held views. In all four revolutions in physics, the replacing theory had greater explanatory coherence than the one it replaced.[19]

An expanding universe

Einstein's General Theory of Relativity implied an expanding universe. But, says Smoot, Einstein was not happy with a beginning at a single point, which made it impossible to know what happened before. He therefore proposed a cosmic constant to counteract gravitational attraction, thus leaving us with a static cosmos. His equations predicted a dynamic universe, but for once he didn't trust them.[20]

Edwin Hubble in 1924 from studies of the Andromeda nebula was able to calculate that its distance from earth put it outside our galaxy. Astronomers were then able to recognize nebulae as separate galaxies. The picture of a cosy universe no larger than our galaxy could no longer be held. Hubble also built on Vesto Melvin Slipher's observations, which had uncovered the first evidence of an expanding universe. In 1912, Slipher noted that there was a shift towards the red end of the spectrum in the light received from galaxies. One possibility was that this indicated that they were moving away from us. Hubble built on the red shift in light coming from distant galaxies and produced Hubble's Law –

that there is a direct correlation between the distance to a galaxy and its red shift. The evidence was clear, the universe was expanding. He calculated that galaxies were moving away from earth at up to 25,000 miles/sec. On this basis the universe had a beginning, which Hubble calculated to be about two thousand million years Before the Present (BP). Einstein recognized the truth of this and said in 1930 that his disbelief of his own equations was his 'greatest blunder'.[21]

In spite of this evidence, Fred Hoyle, Thomas Gold, and Hermann Bondi in the late 1940s and early 1950s presented the idea of a steady state universe. They conceived of the continuous creation of matter which guaranteed a homogenous universe in space and time. They argued that this theory was compelling, for it is only in such a universe that the laws of physics are constant. It removed the problem of a Big Bang beginning where the laws of physics would not apply, and also it had the advantage that it did not have to contemplate the question of 'before' creation. Hoyle included as one of his reasons for accepting this hypothesis that it did not require a god, and was furthest away from the account of creation in Genesis 1, although we might observe that the hypothesis of continuous creation does not contradict the concept of an ever-caring creator.

Confirmation for the view of an expanding universe came through radio astronomy in 1963 when quasars were identified moving away at 150,000 miles/sec. As a result of these findings the age of the universe was estimated at some 10,000 million years BP. The steady state theory of Gold and Bondi was again questioned by the discovery, by Arno Penzias and Robert Wilson in 1964, of background heat radiation in the universe. This background radiation in the universe was seen to be the relic of the Big Bang fireball which marked the beginning of this expanding universe. This thermal radiation has a temperature of 2.7° Absolute or $-270.3°$ Celsius, which although very cold is the left-over 'heat' of the Big Bang itself.[22]

Further confirmation came in 1977 through research carried out by the U-2 spy plane! It carried a differential microwave radiometer high up in the atmosphere, from where it monitored cosmic background radiation in space. This was shown to be remarkably smooth – the apparently homogenous afterglow of the Big Bang.

So we can suggest that the universe has a biography – a beginning, and an end yet to be written.

Our solar system is part of this story. It formed from the rotating disc of dust and gas of a solar nebula. There were planetesimals (from a few metres to the size of Mars) from which the planets accreted. It appears that planets have different compositions because they gathered together different populations of planetesimals. Stuart Ross Taylor notes the unique nature of the earth-moon system:

> The evidence appears decisive that the Moon formed towards the end of the period of planetary accretion through the collision of a Mars-sized impactor with the Earth, and that the material forming the Moon came not from the terrestrial mantle, but from the metal-poor silicate mantle of the impactor. Such an event would have removed any pre-existing atmosphere, and melted the terrestrial mantle, with consequences for mantle crystallisation and evolution which have yet to be worked out in detail.[23]

There are many unusual features about the solar system. It is probably unique, and other planetary systems must be expected to differ substantially from our own. When it formed, the universe was already at least 10,000 million years old. Countless stars had formed and died since the Big Bang and had enriched the interstellar medium in the heavier elements. Only hydrogen, helium, and a little lithium and beryllium were produced in the Big Bang; the heavier elements, from which the earth was constructed and which comprise 2 per cent of the solar system, were formed in nuclear reactions in stellar interiors and supernovae.[24] Our solar system lies in one arm of the spiral galaxy of the Milky Way, which is one of 10^{11} galaxies, each containing about 10^{11} stars. It is interesting to hear Stuart Ross Taylor comment:

> This placing of the Earth and the Solar System, itself possibly unique, in a rather distant corner of the Universe, has implications for the position of *Homo sapiens* in the Universe which have not yet been accommodated in most philosophical, mythological or religious systems.[25]

Th evolution of this complex solar system is not easy to explain. There are many chance factors, which include the initial size of the nebula, its detailed evolution, the early formation of Jupiter (a crucial part of the scenario), and the many random collisions, one of which tipped Uranus on its side, another of which stripped off a major part of the silicate mantle of Mercury, while a third formed our satellite, the Moon.[26]

The birth of the universe

It was Georges-Henri Lemaître who, as early as 1927, took the implications of Slipher and Hubble's work and suggested a single primordial atom that began dividing to form the universe – beginning in an explosion. It should be noted at this point that it is space that is expanding, not the universe expanding into space. Lemaître's hypothesis began to explain not only the origin of the universe, but also the origin of the elements that made up the universe (known to be 75% hydrogen, 25% helium, and 1% all other elements). Evidence from many disciplines has come together this century: Becquerel (radioactivity); J. J. Thomson (discovery of the electron); Rutherford (structure of the atom); William Draper Harkins (the relative abundance of elements with odd and even numbers); Cecilia Payne-Gaposchkin (discovery that the sun is almost entirely hydrogen, and that heat comes not from atomic fission but from nuclear fusion – the coming together of two hydrogen nuclei into a helium nucleus). Such nuclear fusion might explain the origin of elements.

After concluding that the interior of the sun and other stars were not hot enough to fuse light elements into an abundance of heavier elements, Carl Friedrich von Weizsacker, in 1938, suggested that this may have been achieved in a superhot primordial 'fireball'.[27]

In 1965 Roger Penrose showed that singularities are not mathematical concepts, but actually exist in the real universe. He suggested the presence of 'black holes', which are the location of collapsed stars (destroyed in the explosive violence of a supernova) which leave a density so great that light cannot escape its gravitational pull. The matter of the star is compressed into a region of zero volume, so that the density of matter and the curvature of space-time become infinite. This is the nature of a singularity.[28] Stephen Hawking realized that the reverse would also hold true and in 1970 Penrose and Hawking together postulated a physical singularity as the beginning of the universe. Penrose and Hawking suggested that the universe originated as a singularity – a boundary point at the beginning of space-time, when the whole universe was concentrated at one point. Here, the density of the universe would be infinitely large, its size infinitely small, and its energy infinitely high. This singularity is the point from which the universe has expanded following a Big Bang explosion.

In 1950, Martin Ryle had discovered radio emissions from nearby galaxies. When the distribution of radio sources in space were plotted they were not uniform; the more distant they were, the more numerous they were. Thus the density of radio galaxies was greater in the past. In 1977 a differential microwave radiometer aboard a U-2 spy plane revealed that our galaxy is moving at 600 km/sec under the gravitational attraction of some distant, massive concentration of galaxies. Smoot concludes that the universe turned out to be 'much more structured than anyone had guessed, with galaxies existing as components of large conglomerations rather than being distributed uniformly through space'.[29] Yet the cosmic background radiation was seen to be smooth.

After a detective-novel-type investigation, in 1992 wrinkles/fluctuations in the background radiation were identified and confirmed at the edge of the universe. When these wrinkles were mapped out Smoot was able to say:

> The big bang was correct; inflation theory (rapid expansion in early
> stage of universe) worked; the pattern of the wrinkles was about right
> for structure formation by cold dark matter; and the size of distribution
> would yield the major structures of today's universe, under gravitational
> collapse through 15 billion years.[30]

The result indicated that gravity could have shaped today's universe from the tiny quantum fluctuations that occurred in the first fraction of a second after creation. The discovery of the wrinkles revealed that matter was not uniformly distributed, that it was already structured, thus forming the seeds out of which today's galaxies have developed. Smoot believes that as we converge on the moment of creation the constituents and laws of the universe become ever simpler.

> Cosmology – through the marriage of astrophysics and particle physics
> – is showing us that this complexity (of the universe) flowed from a deep
> simplicity as matter metamorphosed through a series of phase
> transitions. Travel back in time through those phase transitions, and we
> see an ever-greater simplicity and symmetry, with the fusion of the
> fundamental forces of nature and the transformation of particles to ever-
> more fundamental components.[31]

We get back to a situation of the infinitely small point of energy – creation from practically nothing but not from nothing.

Does this mean that we can find a 'Theory of Everything'? The logical answer for non-religious belief in a rational cosmos is that the laws of physics are contingent on a 'Theory of Everything'. A genuine theory of this kind will have to explain not only why the universe came into being, but also why it is the only type of universe in which conscious life could have developed. For we are discovering that if the initial conditions had been different then there could have been a different universe, but not one in which human life would have evolved.

It is these considerations that have lead some modern cosmologists to speak of 'fine tuning', and an anthropic principle. It is often suggested that there is some guiding principle or even 'design' that has allowed complex human life to arise within the universe. There are the laws of physics, the uniformity of the expansion of the universe; its size and age – in excess of 100,000 billion, billion kilometres across and some 15–20 billion years old; and biologists see the universe as biocentric – the presence of chemicals and the laws of physics making life possible. The essential element for life, carbon, is manufactured from helium in large stars and released into the universe by supernova explosions; if this is a mere accident it is the luckiest of coincidences. In short, science is suggesting a 'finely tuned' universe, which from the first conditions is uniquely suitable for life forms like ourselves.[32]

So far it would appear that everything within the realm of science is entirely predictable and certain, determined by well-defined laws. This situation changed at the beginning of this century with the appearance of the quantum theory, which is the fourth of our conceptual revolutions. Max Planck suggested that light, x-rays, and other waves were emitted in packets called quanta or photons. In 1926 Werner Heisenberg showed that this simple picture leads to a surprising consequence when applied to atoms and sub-atomic particles. The position and velocity of these particles cannot be determined at the same time. Particles did not have well-defined positions, but a quantum state, which was a combination of position and velocity. It was also discovered that electrons do not follow a definite path around the nucleus. At the quantum level we leave the world of objects moving along the shortest trajectory to a predetermined goal. We enter instead the quantum world of probabilities instead of certainties, which has been described by Heisenberg's Uncertainty Principle. Quantum mechanics predicts a number of different possible outcomes, and tells us how likely each possibility is. In this way it appears that unpredictability and randomness are introduced into science.

More recently has come the suggestion of 'chaos' within physical systems.[33] Chaos theory looks at complex phenomena which are beyond the grasp of a simple determinism, such as the weather, air turbulence, fluid flow, the human heart-beat, and the electrical activity of the brain.

But again when we get behind the name and look at what is meant by 'chaos theory' we find systems which appear to behave in a random fashion, but which do nevertheless obey the physical laws of the universe. The reason for the apparent chaotic behaviour is that the system is very sensitive to the factors which affect its behaviour. The unpredictability lies in our lack of complete knowledge of the initial conditions, not in the way in which the system behaves in respect to the laws of physics.

It would be a mistake to suggest that unpredictability at quantum level or in chaotic systems either rules out the existence of God, or is the place where God acts in creation. From a theological perspective we can conclude that the appearance of chaos does not conflict with the belief that God can fulfil his purposes through the universe. On the one hand, if God in his omniscience knows the initial conditions of any system, he also knows what their conclusions will be. On the other hand, if God offers a real freedom to his creation, he will expose himself, and therefore make himself vulnerable, to a variety of chance variations within the universe which lead to the conclusions of a system in particular detail.[34]

Theological implications

George Smoot quotes Princeton physicist Freeman Dyson, who said, 'The more I examine the universe and the details of its architecture, the more evidence I find that the universe in some sense must have known we were coming.'[35] Smoot himself says that 'the more we learn, the more we see how it all fits together – how there is an underlying unity to the sea of matter and stars and galaxies that surround us.'[36]

Of our own solar system, geoscientist Stuart Ross Taylor says that it is unlikely that such a sequence of events in the path of evolution, which led to *Homo sapiens*, would be duplicated in another planetary system. 'An unpredictable and random event such as the Cretaceous-Tertiary boundary impact (of a large meteorite), was probably crucial in clearing the scene for mammalian evolution to proceed unhindered by the giant reptiles of the Mesozoic.' A large element of chance has entered the evolution of our present system and has led to the recognition of the inherent difficulties in constructing general theories for the origin of solar systems.

Jaki notes that modern scientists such as Arno Penzias (who has studied background cosmic radiation) and V. F. Weisskopf have pointed to the agreement between modern cosmology and the Judaeo-Christian view of creation. He supports this conclusion with a quotation from a book on relativistic cosmology:

> Most astrophysicists, cosmologists and astronomers agree that the biblical account of the beginning of cosmic evolution, in stressing 'a beginning' and the initial roles of 'void', 'light' and a 'structureless' state, may be uncannily close to the verified evidence with which modern science has already supplied us.[37]

In response to such views and those of fundamentalists, Jaki warns that 'unfortunately for fundamentalists, and concordists of all sorts, the possibility of errors built into scientific theories does not guarantee an error-free reading of Genesis 1.'[38] The latter is neither fable nor history, but a biblical proposition, whose meaning has been overlaid by two thousand years of interpretation. We might also note the danger of linking theology to science, seen in the identification by John Robinson and Paul Tillich of views about God with the (now outmoded) steady state theory of Hoyle, Gold and Bondi.[39]

But now we are faced with the question of whether there has been a single beginning to the universe, whether the universe oscillates in and out of 'imaginary time' through a series of explosions, expansion and collapses, or whether the universe has no boundary.[40] Keith Ward believes that Stephen Hawking is wrong to suggest that if one does not have a beginning to the universe then there is no need for God. Ward correctly points out that we still need to explain the existence of space and time. 'The crucial question remains: does the universe as a whole exist without having any reason or explanation, or because it has to be the way it is, or because it is brought into being and held in being at every moment by a supra-cosmic creator?'[41]

Within a Big Bang model of the beginning of the universe there already existed a vast source of potential energy with a complex of quantum laws describing possible interactions of elementary particles; and the universe, according to one theory, originated by the operation of fluctuations in a quantum field in accordance with those laws. Ward rightly concludes that

> Explaining the complex by resolving into a long succession of simple steps leaves the problem of explaining why all those simple steps accumulated in such an amazingly organised way. Saying that the very first step was rather simple is no help at all, when one at once has to add

that it needed the addition of a huge number of co-ordinated simple steps to get the universe as we now have it.[42]

The fact that there is a lot of time in which to do it does not give the explanation.

On the other hand, while some modern cosmologists can suggest that a finely tuned origin of the universe is indicative of 'design', this does not in itself necessarily imply a 'designer'. To believe in a divine designer is a step of faith, and so scientists who do not want to invoke a designer have an alternative; they search for a Grand Unified Theory or a Theory of Everything. However, when it comes to the laws and initial conditions of a universe in which human beings evolve, a fine tuning and high precision is required that leaves a designer as a compelling suggestion. Some cosmologists, irrespective of belief, are now seeing humanity as an integral part of the universe – the Anthropic Principle. Modern cosmology in its investigations of the universe and in the questions that those studies are raising gives new scope to the old religious arguments about design. The discoveries of modern cosmology are not inconsistent with the conclusion that a universe whose initial conditions were finely tuned has been designed to produce human life, which is conscious, aware, and able to contemplate the universe. The alternative to God-given purpose is not 'brute chance' but the 'brute fact' of design itself. Yet we note that others, like Dawkins, would state that evolution mimics design.

Faced by the ultimate question of the beginning of the universe, Smoot says that science is left contemplating the question: Why these conditions and not others? Or perhaps left to see the truth and treasure of the universe only in its own existence.[43] For the Christian thinker more help will be found through belief in a personal God than in a theory, as the final explanation. It is through the believer's encounter with God that ultimate reality is understood. However, human knowledge of God continues to be imperfect; such knowledge includes mystery. It is because God is known in this way, not because God remains unknown, that we affirm that God cannot be known fully.

5 The Earth Gives up Her Dead – Stories of Fossils and Favoured Species

Let the water teem with living creatures, and let birds fly above the earth.[1]

In *The Annals of the World*, published in 1650, the Irish Archbishop James Ussher bravely determined not only the year but also the day and hour of the creation of the earth. Having traced the genealogies of the Old Testament back to Adam, he added six days, and declared that the Earth was created at 8 am on October 22nd, 4004 BC. But cosmology received a new stimulus with the advent of geology as a science. The publication of James Hutton's *Theory of the Earth* in 1795 was foundational for the new science. He stated that the earth was older than the 6,000 years suggested by biblical scholars. The Bible as a record of geology was carefully set aside as he noted that 'it is not in human record, but in natural history, that we are to look for the means of asserting what has already been'.[2] Hutton concluded that the sediment laid down in oceans was the debris of continents, that these sediments could be metamorphosed by subterranean heat, and that only those agents operating today need be invoked to explain the landforms seen in older rocks. This prepared the way for Charles Lyell (1797–1875), a Scottish geologist, who laid the foundations of all modern geology.

Lyell published his *Principles of Geology* between 1830 and 1833,[3] advocating the principle of uniformitarianism, that is, that past processes operated in the same way as those observed in the world today. This required a much longer past history than the catastrophists suggested. It is significant that Darwin read Lyell's *Principles* on his voyage of discovery.

Charles Lyell's uniformitarianism was greeted with suspicion, as it would naturally lead to a very great age for the earth; and geologists continued to struggle to reconcile their science with the biblical account of creation in Genesis 1. Revd Adam Sedgwick, in his presidential address to the Geological Society of London in 1830, came to the conclusion that 'the vast masses of diluvial gravel, scattered almost over the surface of the earth, do not belong to one violent and transitory period' (referring to the Flood). He added that once more Sacred History had been used in the search for truth in such a manner as to turn it, in the words of Francis Bacon, into a search for the living among the dead.[4] In the 1820s the palaeontologist and clergyman William Buckland could still find a place for the Flood of Noah in the history of faunas, even though Linnaeus, in the 1740s, had identified 5,600 species – which could scarcely have been crammed into the ark. Buckland reconciled geology and Genesis 1 by drawing a distinction between Genesis 1.1 and the verses that follow. 'In the beginning', he surmised, was an epoch of unmeasured time when the physical processes of geology were going on.[5]

Modern cosmology presents us with a picture of an evolving universe, from a Big Bang singularity some 15,000 million years ago to the huge dimensions of galaxies and space that we see today. Earth has its own place within the evolution of the universe: our solar system has been evolving for the last 4,500 million years or so; the oldest known rocks on Earth are dated at about 3,900 million years, and material from meteorites about 4,600 million years. The fossil record presents us with a picture of evolving life forms, from simple algal life in the oceans about 3,200 million years ago to the variety of simple and complex life forms we see in our world today. These include *Homo sapiens*, who is the only life form, as far as we know, with a consciousness that is able to perceive the story of the universe. Before we discuss the origin and development of life we need to understand the evolution of the earth, and especially the crust of the planet, where that life exists.

A dynamic earth

Most of the largest planetesimals (planetary fragments) within our solar system coalesced about 4,500 million years ago, with most of the 100km-sized and smaller objects being accreted in the next 500 million years, and completed by about 3,800 million years ago. This is known from the dating of the last great collisions on the moon, dated from samples collected by the Apollo mission. The oldest rocks on earth are dated at 3,960 million years. The noble gases (helium, neon, argon, krypton and xenon) and hydrogen are far less abundant in the earth relative to their proportions in the whole solar system. It appears that by the time the earth, Venus, Mars and Mercury accreted, the gaseous components of the solar nebula were gone. There is no evidence for a primitive atmosphere of earth composed of gases from the solar nebula.[6] Most of the primitive volatiles originated from the degassing of the molten mantle in the first 500 million years. The presence of water is a problem, as little appears to have been available in the zone of the nebula where the earth formed. Temperatures would not have been low enough for water-ice to exist closer than the present asteroid belt, which exists between the orbits of Mars and Jupiter. It is known that the Carbonaceous chondrites (a type of meteorite) contain 20% water by weight, and it seems likely that most terrestrial water was derived from late accretion of such planetesimals between 4,400 and 3,800 million years ago. However, this raises a further problem: the disruptive effect of such impacts would remove earlier atmospheres and hydrospheres. During the early stages of accretion, the earth heated up and became molten through a number of factors, including the decay of short-lived radioactive isotopes and the continuing impacts of accreting planetesimals. These impacts explain the lack of rocks older than 3,960 million years on earth, after which the crustal plates began to form.[7]

The major geological revolution of the twentieth century has been the developing theory of plate tectonics. At the beginning of the century Alfred Wegener (1880–1931), a German geologist and meteorologist, suggested that the continents had once been together and had drifted apart through time. Wegener suggested that 200 million years ago the continents of Africa, South America, Australia and India were united with Eurasia and North America to form a single super continent that he called 'Pangea'. His suggestion was based on a study of the rocks, the fossils, the indications of past climatic conditions preserved in the rocks (palaeoclimatology), and the major fault and mountain structures he observed at the edges of these continents. Although he was ridiculed in his lifetime, he has been completely vindicated by the research into plate tectonics in the last thirty years. Wegener put forward his ideas for drifting continents in a lecture in 1912 and a book first published in 1915, which was translated into English in 1924 with the title *The Origin of Continents and Oceans*. He suggested that the continents were collected together at the north pole and that their movement away from the pole was the result of gravity. Wegener's mechanism of tidal forces and *Polflucht* (flight from the pole), gravitational slip from the pole, was seen as inadequate. Wegener's opponents saw contraction of the crust, producing lateral forces, as the explanation for major geotectonic features. The distribution of fossil fauna was explained by land bridges; continental and oceanic crusts were considered to be of the same composition; and vertical movements took place through isostasy. (Isostasy is the state in which large blocks of the earth's crust are in equilibrium, as if floating in a liquid. This equilibrium is maintained by the tendency for the crust to move vertically up or down, as it floats on the mantle.)

Wegener's theory of drifting continents remained on the fringe until the 1960s. The production of sea-floor maps during the 1950s by the US Navy led to the recognition of the mid-ocean ridges and subsequently the hypothesis of sea-floor spreading, the widening of the ocean basins caused by the up-flow of mantle material to form new oceanic crust. This was a very different explanation from that of Wegener. In 1965 the recognition of symmetrical stripes of reversed and normal magnetism in the sea floor supported the sea-floor spreading hypothesis.

The paradigm or super-model of plate tectonics was independently conceived by Dan McKenzie and Jason Morgan in 1967. 'It grew out of the application to a spherical Earth of sea-floor spreading with its two corollaries – the mid-oceanic ridges with their symmetrically magnetised strips of ocean floor (the Vine-Matthews-Morley hypothesis) and transform faults (Tuzo Wilson, 1965).'[8] The mid-oceanic ridges are recognized as the surface expression of mantle convection.

When all of the information from the sea floors, together with the stratigraphic, palaeontological and palaeoclimatic data that had supported continental drift, was put together, tectonic plates were recognized, bounded by oceanic ridges (where new crust was being formed), ocean trenches (where one plate descended beneath another and was absorbed into the mantle) and transform faults (where the plates slipped side by side). Finally, the geophysical evidence of rigid crustal plates, of a plastic layer below the crust and of the subduction of the crust below ocean trenches confirmed plate tectonics as a credible hypothesis.

The plate tectonics model proposes that the entire surface of the earth comprises a series of rigid but relatively thin plates, 100–150 kilometres thick. The size of these plates is variable; six major plates cover most of the earth's surface: Eurasian, African, Indian, Pacific, Antarctic and American plates. These plates are seen to be in continuous motion, moving apart or towards or alongside each other at rates of between one and three centimetres a year. This movement is taking place in the more plastic layers, below the brittle upper layers of the crust. When the brittle upper crust moves, it fractures and an earthquake occurs. If we consider, as an example, that the Pacific plate has been moving north-westwards relative to the American plate at some three centimetres a year for most of this century, along the line of the San Andreas Fault, and that that movement has yet to be seen on the surface of the crust, we recognize that a major earthquake is going to occur.[9]

Three types of plate margin have been recognized: a constructive margin (such as the mid-Atlantic ridge, where the plates are moving apart and new material is added to the crust in the form of volcanic rock); a destructive plate margin (such as the oceanic trench of the Aleutian arc between Alaska and the former USSR, where one plate is sliding under another); and a conservative plate margin (such as the San Andreas Fault line, where two plates are sliding past each other, with no material added or lost). These plate margins are the sites of almost all the earthquake and volcanic activity seen in the world today.

On a global scale, the whole crust of the earth has changed and developed through geological time. On a smaller scale, the rocks along the coastline of Great Britain, or in its mountains, river valleys, quarries and mines, present a similar picture of change and development through time. These rocks show the development of different environments and climates, from arctic to equatorial – periods that were quiet when sediment was slowly laid down in calm seas; and times of large scale disruption, when the sea floor was thrown up and folded to form mountains, accompanied by earthquakes and violent volcanic activity. There has been a complex development of the rocks that make up the earth's crust.

The evidence from the study of the earth's crust demonstrates, as clearly as is possible, that our planet has had a long history. It was realized (by Rutherford and Holmes in England, and Boltwood in America) early in the twentieth century that the decay of unstable isotopes to produce stable (radiogenic) isotopes could be used to date rocks and minerals. These unstable radioactive isotopes, over time, decay (change by loss of protons and/or neutrons) to stable isotopes of another element. The development of better mass-spectrometers in the 1950s allowed the measurement of the quantities of such isotopes, and this has led to methods of the measurement of geological time known as radiometric dating. Relatively (relative to the time scale involved) precise and accurate methods of dating are based on the radioactive decay rates of isotopes. Some examples of half-lives (time taken for half of the unstable isotopes to decay):

Parent	Daughter	Half life (years)
^{14}C	^{14}N	5730
^{87}Rb	^{87}Sr	4.88 billion
^{40}K	^{40}Ca	1.40 billion
^{40}K	^{40}Ar	110 million
^{147}Sm	^{143}Nd	108 billion
^{234}U	^{230}Th	248,000
^{235}U	^{207}Pb	704 million
^{238}U	^{206}Pb	4.468 billion[10]

Radiometric dating has established the age of the earth (about 4,550 million years), and of the major changes in its history, and in so doing it has revolutionized our understanding. Through such dating we find that microbial colonies have left fossil records (stromatolites) of life since 3,500 million years ago, the first vertebrates appeared about 530 million years ago, the first land fossils occur at the end of the Silurian (about 395 million years ago), and hominoid species first appeared a mere 1.7 million years ago.

There are, however, limitations for our study of the earth's crust, which have implications for the conclusions we might draw. We cannot directly observe past events in the geological history of the earth, stretching back some 4,600 million years, nor can we directly observe the deeper reaches of the crust and the earth's interior, thousands of kilometres below our feet. We also recognize that, through geological time, periods of crustal movement, marine erosion, metamorphism and igneous intrusion and extrusion have destroyed large parts of the record in the rocks. This means that some geological theories and hypotheses, including that of evolution, are described as models that best fit the facts as we know them.

The living earth

It is widely held that most of the gases of the present atmosphere were derived from gases given off during volcanic eruptions, early in the earth's history. If they were similar to those of modern volcanoes, water vapour and carbon dioxide (CO_2) would have made up the bulk of the volatiles, followed by hydrogen sulphide, carbon monoxide, hydrogen, nitrogen, methane, ammonia, hydrogen fluoride, hydrogen chloride and argon. The lack of molecular oxygen in modern volcanic exhalations has led to the conclusion that the atmosphere in the Archaean (4,500–

2,500 million years ago) was anoxygenic, the free oxygen that we see today having evolved subsequently. The oxygen must have been derived from dissociation of oxides such as CO_2 or H_2O; solar radiation providing the energy source for two possible photochemical reactions, inorganic (photodissociation) and organic (photosynthesis).[11]

Ultraviolet radiation breaks down water vapour to H_2 and O_2. It is assumed that some of this free oxygen helped to form the ozone layer of the primitive atmosphere, which acted as a barrier to further ultraviolet radiation and enabled early life forms to evolve enzymes to deal with toxic oxygen. Larger amounts of oxygen are produced through photosynthesis: low energy light provided the energy for primitive organisms to produce carbohydrates by photosynthesis from water and CO_2, releasing oxygen as a by-product. This reaction occurred in green plants and cyanobacteria (formerly termed blue-green algae).

Although from 4,000 to 2,000 million years ago most of the oxygen produced was used in oxidation or became fixed in carbonate deposits, such as stromatolites, it is generally accepted that free oxygen became abundant in the atmosphere between 2,500 and 2,000 million years ago.

Large quantities of organic carbon were buried in oxidized form as limestone in the period 900–600 million years ago, which indicates that oxygen probably increased substantially during this period. Fossil charcoal from the Devonian suggests a level of 13% for atmospheric oxygen. It is calculated that oxygen levels rose significantly during the Permo-Carboniferous (350–250 million years ago), because of the rise of vascular land plants and the widespread burial of organic matter in vast coal swamps. Oxygen abundance increased to near present-day levels during the Cretaceous and early Tertiary (135–25 million years ago).[12]

There is a close relationship between oxygen levels and the development of life forms. The progressive increase in the molecular oxygen content of the atmosphere triggered off major biological innovations that enabled life to advance and diversify. By about 2,000 million years ago, oxygen reached 10% of present atmospheric level; by 1,500 million years ago it had increased to such an extent that the first oxygen-employing *eukaryotes* (organisms whose cells contain a nucleus within which lie the chromosomes) appeared in oxygenated waters. By 700–600 million years ago the first metazoa appeared (ediacara – jelly-fish, worms and sponges), complex multicellular organisms that require oxygen for their growth. The Cambrian period (570–510 million years ago) was a period when skeletal *eukaryotes* usurped the function of *prokaryotes* (single-celled organisms with no distinct nucleus, such as bacteria and blue-green algae) in removing the CO_2 greenhouse gas through the precipitation of calcium carbonate.[13]

Today there is a growing awareness of the environmental peril of greenhouse gases, which we will discuss at greater length in Chapter 8. The main contributors to the greenhouse effect are carbon dioxide (70%), methane (23%) and nitrous oxide (7%). For several thousand years before the beginning of industrialization, around 1750, a steady balance was maintained, such that the concentration of CO_2 in the atmosphere as measured from ice cores kept within about 10 parts per million of a mean value of about 280 ppmv (parts per million by volume). This has increased by 25% to about 350 ppmv in the 1990s as a result of industrialization and the destruction of forests. Methane has also increased dramatically during the last hundred years, mainly from sewage treatment, extraction of fossil fuels and rice paddies.[14]

An inhabited earth

In the world today there are more than 350,000 species of plants, of which approximately 250,000 are flowering plants, 10,000 are ferns and trees, and 60,000 are algae and fungi. There are 1,200,000 species of animals of which about 900,000 are arthropods (mostly beetles and insects), 120,000 are molluscs (snails, winkles, oysters and other shells), and 45,000 are chordates (animals with a backbone), which include us. Fossil evidence of life is distributed through over 120 kilometres thickness of sedimentary rocks, which have accumulated in many ocean basins through geological time. It appears, then, that this fossil record should give vital clues to understanding the rich variety of species that we see around us today. But what is the origin of this diverse life that is found in the rocks, and in the world today? How did it begin? Why did it develop in the sea first and then on the land and in the air? The origin of carbon-based life has been a puzzle that has intrigued biologists and palaeontologists.

Whether the origin of life is natural or the result of miraculous intervention, we have a pointer towards purpose in a universe that produces both amino acids and nucleic acids in some primordial ocean. The precise way in which life originated is an open question, yet to be solved by science – the indications of experimental work suggest that a natural answer may well be found.

Life as we observe it today is the end product of cosmic and terrestrial evolution over the last fifteen thousand million years. Cesare Emiliani maintains that 'far from being a miracle, life is a *necessary* and *inevitable* consequence of the way the world originated and evolved'.[15] He suggests that life may have begun a number of times during the early turbulent period 4,500 to 3,800 million years ago, each new start wiped out by the latest asteroidal impact. Life took hold when these impacts ceased, about 3,800 million years ago. He believes that life originated when methane was the dominant gas in the atmosphere, as demonstrated by the Urey-Miller experiment, which produced amino acids.[16] However, while amino acids are important building blocks, in order to have the simplest forms of life many other organic compounds must be present and conditions favourable for their interaction must exist. This leads Morris to comment that 'there is an immense gulf between this soup of relatively simple molecules and a cell capable of division and replication'.[17] Interest more recently has focused on clay minerals as possible templates for coding of information; and the possible role of hydrothermal systems connected with oceanic spreading plate margins, in the origin of life on earth.

What happened in the first 800 million years of earth history is shrouded in uncertainty. Nitrogen, water vapour and CO_2 were the major components of the early atmosphere, the CO_2 preventing the new earth from freezing, for without its 'greenhouse effect' the less luminous sun of 4,000 million years ago would have been unable to warm the planet sufficiently (more fine-tuning). The earliest known fossil life that has been found has been bacterial and algal material, together with the presence of amino acids, in rocks as old as 3,200 million years. However, the bulk of present-day mammals have developed in the last 20 million years.

From that starting point in the primordial ocean we now need to consider how and why life developed as it did. Plant life on dry land only existed from about 420 million years ago. It was only at this stage that the lethal ultraviolet levels were cut out by the atmosphere, so allowing plant life to develop. Berkner and Marshall[18] suggest that the evolution of life on earth is related to critical levels of oxygen in the evolving atmosphere.

By 600 million years ago the ozone level would have been sufficient to cut out the DNA-inactivating ultraviolet radiation. This would have opened up the oceans to the development and growth of photosynthesizing phytoplankton, which would in turn lead to a large increase in the amount of oxygen in the atmosphere. By 420 million years ago the oxygen content of the atmosphere had reached a level where land plants could survive. Their growth lead to further, more rapid, increase in oxygen levels. It has been suggested[19] that at this time the oxygen level had reached 10% of its present-day level. The result gave rise to an immediate evolutionary response with many groups of land plant and animal species developing from their marine counterparts.

Lovelock says, 'The climate and chemical properties of the earth now and throughout its history seem always to have been optimal for life. For this to have happened by chance is as unlikely as to survive unscathed a drive blindfold through rush-hour traffic.'[20] His concept of Gaia draws on the same supporting fine-tuning as we discussed in consideration of the anthropic principle, in Chapter 4.

An evolving earth

Darwin's theory of evolution by natural selection (*The Origin of the Species by Means of Natural Selection or The Preservation of Favoured Races in the Struggle for Life*, published in 1859) was a direct challenge to the dominant scientific theory of the early nineteenth century. Most scientists of Darwin's day held that species were individual creations of God, even though geologists were beginning to suggest a very old earth. In 1809 Jean Lamarck had suggested the transmutation of species, based on a model of increasing complexity and a capacity to inherit acquired characteristics that were useful to the particular environment. Although Darwin did not reject such inheritance, he considered that evolution was change that results from random variation and natural selection. Darwin rejected Lamarck's ideas because they did not explain, for example, why tree frogs should climb trees. Reading Malthus' essay on population growth (1838) led Darwin to recognize that 'only organisms well adapted to their environments and to reproduction would survive the struggle for existence'.[21]

The conceptual revolution comes through the view that there is a commonality of descent through evolution rather than a hierarchy of taxa (plant and animal groups). William Paley's view[22] was that the complexities of fossil and living species were explained as individual works of the divine creator. Darwin's main hypotheses, that organic beings undergo natural selection and that species of organic beings have evolved, enabled him to explain a host of facts, from geographical distribution of similar species to the existence of vestigial organs. Thagard is right to point out that 'Darwin's theory does not strictly contradict the existence of God, since one can always maintain that it was God who created the universe with laws that eventually resulted in natural selection and biological evolution ... however, Darwin's theory decisively undermined a powerful argument for God's existence based on the adaption of organisms.'[23] In 1871 Darwin, in *The Descent of Man*, extended his thesis to include human beings. This implied that they must also have evolved and were not a special creation.

The concept of evolution began with Lamarck, but Darwin provided the theory of a natural mechanism by which it might be actualized. Yet neither Lamarck nor Darwin were able to show how characteristics of the favoured species were passed on from one generation to another. The answer was found in the middle of the nineteenth century by the Abbot of Brunn, Gregor Johann Mendel (1822–84) in Moravia, through the breeding of garden peas in a monastery garden, but it did not become known until the end of the century. By crossing pea plants he arrived at the concept of dominant and recessive genes, and formulated the laws of heredity. His results lay unnoticed until 16 years after his death. Mendelian genetics combined with Darwinian natural selection provided the means by which evolution might be understood to progress.

The primary gene products are the direct consequence of a rather simple chemical process that has been worked out in the revolution of molecular biology begun in 1955 with the elucidation of the structure of DNA by James Watson and Francis Crick. At this level, inherited characters can be said to be determined by the genes carried by an individual. Once we leave the primary gene product level, however, the occurrence, speed and path of chemical processes in the body are affected to varying extents by environmental influences.[24] We might note at this point in the argument that Berry maintains that human beings are not, contrary to popular belief, captives of their genes. He argues that there is no such thing as a behavioural gene, but that 'every behaviour is the result of interactions between inherited and environmental factors'.[25] People have different natures and problems but no behaviour is inevitable.

A number of questions now arise, some of which are: Can life be explained fully in terms of physics and chemistry? Can the apparent self-determination and goal-orientation of organisms be accounted for fully by physics and chemistry? Although Richard Dawkins[26] begins with an entirely reductionist view, which sees life merely in terms of its chemical and physical components, he concludes that there must be some guiding mechanism in the otherwise chance development of complex life forms. When faced with the question of how something so complex as the human eye could evolve, his answer is that it has done so *by one small step at a time* through the immensity of geological epochs. Dawkins[27] concludes that the essence of life is statistical improbability on a colossal scale. Thus, whatever the explanation for life might be, 'it cannot be chance', by which he means 'pure naked chance'. Cumulative selection, he maintains, is a different form of chance, 'chance at every step'; it is what he calls 'tamed chance'. To 'tame' chance means to break down the very improbable into less improbable small components arranged in series. However, he also states that there must be a 'mechanism' for guiding each step in the same particular direction, otherwise 'the sequence of steps will career off in an endless random walk'. This guiding mechanism for Dawkins is the urge for survival, and so a 'non-random' aiming at a target of survival at every step.

We have every right, however, to question the explanatory power of this theory. Is such small-scale non-random survival really sufficient to explain the convergence of evolutionary patterns on the separated continents of Eurasia-Africa, North-South America, and Australia whereby similar species have developed in isolation from each other over the last 200 million years? It is significant that Dawkins is looking for an immanent principle by which evolution takes place. He finds it in *gradual* natural selection alone, but for a Christian believer the guiding mechanism will be expressed as the involvement of the immanent God with his creation. The heart of this issue is not whether natural selection through non-random survival takes place, but whether it is a *sufficient* mechanism to lead to the development of conscious self-aware human beings. We might then suggest that the immanent purpose of the creator, working *through* natural selection and non-random survival, appears to be more reasonable than chance, even if it is a 'tamed' kind of chance.

When we come to consider human beings, the modern geneticist Sam Berry, who is a Christian, says that the animal relationship of human kind is inescapable. We share all but 0.7% of the DNA of the two extant chimpanzee species. We are closer in relation to chimps than the two species of gibbon are to each other (they differ by 2.2% of their DNA).

In the biblical accounts of creation we understand that we are linked to natural creation: created on the same day (Genesis 1); and of the same substance (Genesis 2). But we are also distinct: *imago Dei*

(Genesis 1); and with God's Spirit/breath (Genesis 2).[28] Berry has sought to consider whether or not a special creation of human beings 'in the image of God', is possible.[29] He considers the later stages in the development of hominids. *Homo erectus* was widely distributed in the Upper Pleistocene, about a million years BP; an upright walker, meat eater, tool maker, belonging to the 'Great hand axe' culture. They did not differ greatly from *H. sapiens* and seem to have overlapped with them. There are a number of well documented intermediary forms, from 300 to 150,000 years BP, including Swanscombe (lower Thames valley), Vertessozollos (Hungary), Steinheim (Germany), and Montmaurin and Fontechevade (France). Berry states that the gene pool of any species is the result of the interactions of the past individuals of that species with all their previous environments. If human beings were instantaneously created, it follows that all their behaviour, reactions and relations would be the consequence of God's intention, Adam's sin, and the short time since the Garden of Eden. Although possible, Berry maintains that this is almost certainly untrue, and also that it raises theological difficulties: i) God does not use the whole of his creation for his purpose; ii) it requires our relationship with God to be controlled genetically, as genes must be created to enable response to God. Berry concludes:

> There are three possible views about human origins: as 'nothing but' a highly evolved ape; as 'nothing but' a special creation of God made complete in every respect; or as an ape inbreathed by God's Spirit, with an evolutionary history but with a unique relationship with the Creator. Only the last can incorporate both a sensible understanding of Scripture and the findings of science ... [and do] justice to the God of the Bible, who is both creator and sustainer.[30]

There comes a stage in the development of hominids when they are conscious of, and able to relate to, the creator. The biblical account would suggest that this is an act of God's self-revelation, when human beings have developed to a point when such a revelation might be received.

We need to remember at this stage in our discussion the limits of our knowledge of the fossil record, and therefore of the information in support of the theory of evolution.

The earliest life forms were mostly microbial. One problem in interpretation is that 'organisms with radically different biochemistries, tolerance of oxygen, ability to utilise substrates and so forth are often morphologically indistinguishable.'[31] Thus radical evolution may not be observable (the 'Volkswagen Syndrome', where the outer shell remains unchanged but under the bonnet there are significant changes). Long-term evolution cannot be investigated experimentally, but hypotheses can be tested against the fossil evidence.

One important new proposition is that of punctuated evolution,[32] whereby most morphological evolution was limited to small, geographically isolated populations, undergoing rapid divergence from their parent populations, while large well established species populations remained morphologically static.

It is also clear that much morphological evolution is too rapid to be faithfully registered in the fossil record: the latter yields only the vague outlines of highly dynamic patterns. The conclusions of palaeontologists are therefore restricted by the morphology and limited preservation of fossils. While the fossil record is often incomplete and complete evolutionary lineages cannot be shown, there is sufficient evidence of changes from one species to another in successive rock layers to demonstrate that mutation in response to environmental change does take place. Such mutation would form the basis of natural selection.

Theological implications

We live on a dynamic planet with a long history of development, in which the accretion of planetesimals, the formation of a primitive atmosphere, the origin and evolution of plant and animal life, and the configuration of continents and oceans, have all played their part. Ruth Page emphasizes the web of interconnectedness and interrelationships within ecosystems. This organic pattern, within the cosmos, has replaced the chain of cause and effect, with God as the first cause (cf. Aquinas), and gives a sense of coherence, meaning and purpose to life.[33] This web is part of the whole geological history of the earth. Unlike the chain, this picture is based upon scientific research rather than on philosophical speculation. This picture is global and is not confined to one belief system.

David Atkinson[34] is right to state that we do not have a ready-made world, but the picture of an emerging creation. We can see evolution as a God-given capacity, the same as fruitfulness, fertility and development. The dangers arise when evolution leads us into a reductionism of nothing but physics and chemistry. Atkinson notes that the end of that path is demonstrated by Jacques Monod's conclusion of the meaning of life based on molecular biology:

> The ancient covenant is in pieces; man at last knows that he is alone in the unfeeling immensity of the universe, out of which he emerged only by chance.[35]

This is a move beyond biology or evolution to a faith in no god. Berry is convinced that evolutionary change has occurred and that its mechanism is along the lines described by neo-Darwinian theory; but he is equally confident that God created the world, through this process. Nowhere in the Bible are we told the mechanisms God used to carry out his work; indeed it is only by faith that we know that God is involved.[36]

The predominance of reason over beliefs was emphasized and formalized by the positivism of the Vienna Circle, in the 1920s and 1930s, which was avowedly atheistic. The positivists wanted to show that each science could be reduced to the one below – that is, that entities at a given level could be entirely explained in terms of the operation of its parts, the entities at the next level down.[37] While this has clear advantages for the conduct of one form of experimental research in science, it runs into problems when seeking to explain complex inter-active systems. We might consider the example of human freedom: are we really free, or controlled by the physics of our sub-atomic parts?

We discover that there are questions that are answered at the level we are considering; questions that can only be answered by reference to a lower level; and also questions that can only be answered at a higher level – boundary questions. Some of the most fundamental boundary questions can be answered by theology, for example questions of meaning and purpose.[38]

Dawkins is certainly right in his criticism of William Paley's biological argument, which views each animal and plant species as a special act of God's creative power. Paley could not imagine how plants and animals could have developed without the mechanism of God's particular creation applied to each one; this is in essence a 'God of the gaps' argument. Nancey Murphy is right to state that much of the resistance to evolutionary biology can be traced to limited views of divine action. The problem with Enlightenment thinking was that it led to natural laws being seen as distinct from any act of God. This was different from the medieval view of God as the primary cause of the secondary causes (recognized as laws). The result was that natural laws were seen as a denial of divine action, and so evolution was seen as natural rather than as God working out his creative purpose through the evolutionary process.[39] She concludes:

For the materialist the cosmic process itself is ultimate. For us, there is a longer story, beginning before the Big Bang and continuing beyond the various 'ends' that physical cosmologists can project – a story whose loveliness must in its telling 'exhaust all skill and consume all words.'[40]

The fundamental question is whether the universe has purpose. Dawkins denies that the evolution of complex life forms indicates purpose, but we must question whether this denial can be sustained with regard to the human mind. Is the human mind merely a computer, part of a mathematical universe? Or does the evolution of conscious human beings indicate the purpose of a supreme and transcendent mind?

In a fascinating study of the mind, Roger Penrose suggests[41] that consciousness is associated with seeing necessary truths, and that the hallmark of consciousness is thus a non-algorithmic (i.e. non-computable, not able to be worked out by a specific calculation) forming of judgements. Consciousness appears to be the element in the brain which allows us to see and appreciate what mathematical truth is, and this in itself demonstrates that the brain is not a computer. We might add to this the perception of aesthetic beauty in art, music, and nature, or the emotions of hope, fear, anxiety or despair. Penrose concludes with these remarks:

> Consciousness seems to me to be such an important phenomenon that I cannot believe that it is something just 'accidentally' conjured up by a complicated computation. It is the phenomenon whereby the universe's very existence is made known.[42]

Even though much of what is involved in mental activity might work in the same way as a computer, there are other characteristics of the conscious mind.

A conscious mind requires explanation, and it is not unreasonable for theistic believers to find this in the conscious mind of a purposeful designer. In fact, 'purpose' becomes the key issue in the argument. It does not take religious belief to recognize the features of design in the universe. When cosmologists speak of the Anthropic Principle, they are speaking of an inherent design. We might even suggest that Dawkins' and Gould's models of evolution require a guiding principle to prevent evolutionary changes running down so many blind alleys. But design does not of course prove the presence of a designer, and for cosmologists it is often a way of speaking about inherent principles and laws. A step towards a creator is made when we speak about purpose, though this too may not necessarily imply a personal giver of purpose; for some cosmologists, who are not religious believers, are also tempted to speak of 'purpose'. The step of faith lies in moving from design and purpose to belief in a creator, whose mind and purpose are written into the evolution of human life. But the recent evidence of research in the physical and biological sciences would seem to make such a step of faith a reasonable one to take.

The question thus presses perhaps harder than ever before on the impartial observer, as to whether a universe that has seen the evolution of conscious human life requires the presence of a purposeful mind as its origin.

6 What Sort of God and How Has God Been Perceived by Human Beings?

Where were you when I laid the earth's foundation? Tell me, if you understand.[1]

In spite of the dialogue between science and theology, there have been, and still are, conflicts between these two fundamental sources of human knowledge about the world. The conflict is at its most acute between the scientific materialist and the biblical literalist. From the scientific side, science is seen as the only source of reliable, factual knowledge, while religion is seen to be subjective, emotional, traditional (i.e. old-fashioned), and superstitious. From the side of biblical literalism, science is seen as deceived and deceiving, and centred upon sinful human beings, while uncritical biblical study provides the only sure truth. Both of these attitudes are the result of a failure to understand fully what the other is saying.

'It is not possible to be intellectually honest or to be a true scientist and believe in gods,' said Peter Atkins, professor of chemistry at Oxford. Religious belief, he thought, was 'outmoded and ridiculous'. Belief in gods was a 'worn out but once useful crutch in mankind's journey towards truth ... We consider the time has come for that crutch to be abandoned ... To say that "God made the world" is simply a more or less sophisticated way of saying that we don't understand how the universe originated. A god, in so far as it is anything, is an admission of ignorance.'[2]

Meanwhile, on the other side of the world, an Australian geologist took fundamentalist Christians to court for teaching creationism (a literal interpretation of Genesis 1—9). Professor Ian Plimer of the School of Earth Sciences at the University of Melbourne accused creationists of selling 'misleading and deceptive' materials.[3] In the United States there has been a long tradition of creationism versus evolution, ever since a Tennessee biology teacher, John Scopes, was tried

81

in 1925 (the infamous 'Monkey Trial') for breaking the law by teaching evolution. This continues today with some schools refusing to teach anything but 'creation science'.

Dispelling the conflict myth

The survival of religion may support its fundamental truth that no science can undermine; or that the psychological needs of humans demand a place for religion in spite of scientific discovery, as Peter Atkins believes; or it survives as a focus of collective identity – merely a sociological function.

J. W. Draper's *History of the Conflict Between Religion and Science* (1875) put forward the view of contending powers, of intellect against traditional faith. Brooke contends that this was essentially a diatribe against the Roman Catholic faith, in response to the decree of papal infallibility in 1870.[4] Similarly, A. D. White in his book, *A History of the Warfare of Science with Theology in Christendom* (1895), sought to present the Darwin debate as a struggle between religion and science. Both of these authors failed to recognize the efforts of those who saw science and religion as complementary. For example, some saw God working through nature; others suggested that God was the primary cause of the various secondary causes that were being discovered; even T. H. Huxley recognized a wider teleology not touched by the doctrine of evolution. Complementarity between theology and science was still possible for Huxley, even if he chose to remain agnostic. Brooke criticizes both Draper and White for their failure to understand past scientific hypotheses in their historical context.[5]

We might note that Copernicus' heliocentric solar system was contrary to the Aristotelian mathematics established for 1,500 years. The argument that developed was more to do with rival science, although we should note that the church supported Aristotle's views, as we shall see in the next section in the views of Aquinas. But sometimes we draw the wrong conclusions from history. It is true that Galileo's discoveries brought him into conflict with the Catholic Church. His translation of Copernicus' theory into Italian became popular reading in the universities, and soon rival academics were seeking to persuade the Catholic Church to ban Copernicanism. In 1616, despite the arguments presented by Galileo, the Church authorities declared that Copernicanism was erroneous and forced Galileo to recant. However, Brooke, as an historian, notes that it was suggested that Galileo was brought before the Pope because of insults he had meted out to Jesuits rather than his scientific views. Similarly, he believes that Charles Lyell left Cambridge, not because of a dispute over the Flood of Noah, which he rejected, but because he did not receive the remuneration he had expected.

In the case of Darwin, *The Origin of the Species* had a notable list of supporters. It included Huxley, the major zoologist of his time, Hooker, the finest botanist, and Lyell, the greatest geologist. Also in support were Herbert Spencer, Sir John Lubbock (later Lord Avebury), Canon Tristram, who had studied the animals recorded in the Bible, Alfred Newton, the ornithologist, and Charles Kingsley, clergyman and novelist. In later years support also came from Cardinal John Henry Newman and Archbishop William Temple. Darwin was opposed by the naturalist Philip Gosse, who was a member of the Plymouth Brethren; by the geologist Adam Sedgwick; and by the comparative anatomist and palaeontologist Richard Owen. There was opposition from the side of the Church, which recognized that Darwin's conclusions were incompatible with a doctrine of creation deduced from a literal understanding of Genesis. Owen was the scientific mind behind the religious opposition to Darwin at the Oxford meeting of the British Association in 1860. But while Bishop Wilberforce's arguments were largely demolished by Huxley, it was the bishop who won the support of the audience, according to Sir Joseph Hooker. Scientists and theologians were on both sides of the argument. We should be aware that people enter the debate between science and religion for a variety of reasons, including both the scientific and the religious. Such debates are a feature of the complex social interactions between people.

There were real intellectual arguments taking place, of which the Huxley–Wilberforce debate over human origins in the nineteenth century is a good example. There was a social transformation taking place in which clergy were losing their intellectual standing in the nation. One reason for this was the professionalization of the sciences, with a resulting diminution in the part played in scientific research by clergy in their spare time. Science increasingly was focused on prosperity, economic strength, and military security, rather than discovering God's good creation.[6] So it would be fair to believe that Huxley would relish having a go at a bishop in his desire to promote the professionalism of science; and in the same way, for the bishop an opportunity of demonstrating the clergy's ability to address the intellectual issues of the day.

As we noted in Chapter 5, Nancey Murphy states that much of the resistance to evolutionary biology can be traced to the limited views of divine action. The natural laws recognized by science were seen as a denial of divine action, and so evolution was seen as natural rather than as God working out his creative purpose through the evolutionary process.[7] We can accept the evolutionary model but there is a need to show where the legitimate claims of evolutionary biology end. Science itself needs to be distinguished from the religious and metaphysical speculations that some atheistic scientists append (see, for example, Peter Atkins above).

It is the level of explanation that is important, and Murphy, in her central thesis, claims that biological evolution requires the higher level of explanation which only theology can give. She notes that there are two models in science: i) the hierarchical model, in which the higher sciences permit a study of more complex organizations or systems of the entities at the next level down; and ii) the opposite direction of explanation – the reductionist approach of the logical positivists, who showed that each science could be reduced to the one below. Murphy considers that biological evolution is one of the fundamental boundary questions that can be addressed by theology, as it raises questions of meaning and purpose. The alternative is a universe that is without meaning, as Steven Weinberg once suggested.[8] Cosmology and physics raise such boundary questions, and rather than a conflict model, we can recognize, along with Murphy, that theology can often be an overarching explanation for other sciences.

Philosophers grapple with the nature of the universe

Thomas Aquinas (1225–74), in line with Aristotle, saw the world as being composed of real things which act as true causes. They are complete as far as they go, but must be seen in the light of the 'First Cause'. So Aquinas believed that we can arrive at the conclusion that God exists from a deeply considered acceptance of the world about us. His celebrated five ways of thinking about God's existence take up five general observations about the universe, namely its change, dependence, contingency, limited perfection, and utility. He infers a changeless changer, an uncaused cause (the First Cause, cf. Aristotle's Unmoved Mover), a necessary being, a completely perfect one, and an ultimate end; all this combines to form a definition of God. Aquinas' five ways include what later became known as the 'cosmological' argument (God as the ultimate cause of the cosmos) and the 'teleological' argument (God as the ultimate designer).[9] While Aquinas presents his five ways as if they are proofs of the existence of God, they were only designed to provide a rational defence of an already existing faith in God.

Alongside the great scientific discoveries of the seventeenth and eighteenth centuries there was the flourishing of rational philosophy, which was focused on the world rather than on God. René Descartes (1596–1650), who was a contemporary of the scientists Kepler and Galileo, saw rational argument as the only source of truth. Seeing the mechanistic view of the universe proposed by science, he divided the universe into object and observer, matter and mind, the scientific world of the physical universe and the philosophical world of the mind with its values, beliefs, and emotions (including the soul). John Locke took this a stage further, suggesting that knowledge comes through the physical senses: observation, analysis, and deduction according to reason. Revelation is demoted or discarded in favour of reason.

David Hume (1711–76) believed that truth or falsehood could only be learned from experience, and that the only field of demonstrative reasoning was mathematics. In his *Dialogues Concerning Natural Religion* he acknowledged that the argument from design was the strongest of the traditional 'proofs', but then proceeded to undermine it by some devastating arguments. First, he observed that the universe was more like a living organism than an artefact that had been made, so that order could be said to be immanent in nature itself, rather than being derived from a designer. It was as if the universe was just 'growing' by itself according to its own internal guidelines.

Second, he pointed out that for any universe to exist it must be ordered, and so it will be bound to look as if it were designed.

Third, we know that a watch is designed because we have other mechanisms to compare it with; but the universe is unique and incomparable.

Fourth, we cannot deduce from a finite, imperfect world that there is an infinite, perfect creator; the design argument can only indicate a creator who is one degree different and more clever than we. While the discovery of random mutations and natural selection in the living world seems to confirm Hume's argument, especially the appearance of the world as a 'great animal' rather than a piece of machinery,[10] we must not forget that modern cosmology is presenting us with a new kind of model of design, in the form of a finely tuned universe.

Hume's criticisms of natural theology were taken further by Immanuel Kant (1724–1804), who studied mathematics and physics as well as philosophy. In his *Critique of Pure Reason* (1781) he deals critically with the three speculative proofs of God's existence (the Ontological, Cosmological and Teleological Arguments), arguing that all three types are fallacious.[11] He believed that the Cosmological Argument failed because it assumed that there is not an infinite causal series. Kant considered that the Teleological Argument, or argument from design, was acceptable, but not logically compulsive. Following Hume, he pointed out that it only proves the existence of an architect of the universe whose powers may be remarkable, but not necessarily infinite.

How could theology find a place for the gospel in a world of cause and effect? The answer appears to have been a retreat into the private world of beliefs and values. Schleiermacher (1768–1834) sought to fence off an area of inward religious experience, away from the examination of rational science. This was a protection, but led to the separation of the public world of facts from the private world of faith. He saw the Bible as an account of the religious experiences of the people of God.

This led Feuerbach (1804–72) to draw the conclusion that God is simply the projection of the human ego onto the cosmos.

This dualism, the separation of spiritual and material realms, has been a marked characteristic of western thinking for the last century. It is one that Lesslie Newbigin, through the Gospel and Culture Movement sought to address. I am sure that he was absolutely right when he wrote:

> The greatest intellectual task facing the Church is a new dialogue with science – a dialogue for which the way has been prepared by profound changes in science (especially in physics) during this century.[12]

Science largely presents mechanistic and reductionist ideas of creation, which see the universe as a great machine, understood by reduction to its basic parts. The machine idea changes our relationship to the world, as we become observers, analysts, managers, seeing and operating from outside nature. So this is a dualistic model *par excellence*.[13] The alternative would be an organic and holistic worldview. It is the current ecological crisis that is forcing us to rethink our views of creation and our relationship to it. This reflection can take different forms: scientific or mystical, classical or New Age, religious or postmodern. Ecology is stressing the connectedness of all things, touching on the mystery of life itself.[14] The concept of Gaia, Mother Earth, Mother Nature, World Soul, which disappeared with Enlightenment rationalism, has now re-surfaced with ecology. James Lovelock, the leading advocate of Gaia, stresses the dynamic connection between the physical earth and its life forms; the evolution of life-forms is closely coupled with the evolution of their physical and chemical environment. It is a Whole Earth theory, in which the key perspective is not each particular life form or micro-system, but the overall system – Living Earth – of which each smaller system (microbes, forests, oceans) is but a part. For Lovelock, Gaia theory is the basis of a unified view of the earth and life sciences. Humans are merely one of the species that evolve with the environment – it is Gaia that is special. The Gaia hypothesis draws on the same fine tuning support as does the Anthropic Principle. Lovelock says, 'The climate and chemical properties of the Earth now and throughout its history seem always to have been optimal for life. For this to have happened by chance is as unlikely as to survive unscathed a drive blindfold through rush-hour traffic.'[15] But, for Lovelock, human beings are one part of the interdependent system, having no more right to life than any other species. We will consider the ecological and theological implications of this in Chapter 8.

Paul Davies believes that while science usually leads in the direction of reliable knowledge, the breathtaking answers of science still leave unanswered the question 'Why?'[16] The universe may well show astonishing ingenuity in its construction, and human beings certainly appear to be part of the scheme of things, but we are left with the question of whether the chain of explanation ends with God or some super-law. Stephen Hawking remarks that 'we find ourselves in a bewildering world. We want to make sense of what we see around us and to ask: what is the nature of the universe? what is our place in it and where did it and we come from? why is it the way it is?'[17] Hawking is concerned above all else to find one law that will ultimately explain the origin and nature of the universe, and so unveil 'the mind of God'.

A revived argument from design

The main features of the modern design argument are as follows.

An ordered universe

Penrose says that for some reason, the universe was created in a very special (low entropy) state.[18] If there was enough time stars and galaxies, and even human life, might form accidentally in a universe, but the time needed is estimated to be in excess of 10^{800} years (10 followed by 800 zeros!). Our observation of this universe is only possible because we exist, and our existence is either a miracle or an incredible accident. This leads cosmologists to discuss the Anthropic Principle.

The nature of the universe as an inter-related organism

From a scientific perspective we see that under the diversity and complexity of the universe there is an underlying unity, an interconnectedness in its fundamental forces and principles. This would suggest one unifying source of creativity or origin. For us to see the universe we might reasonably suggest that it must have developed with us in mind. Berry, speaking of Gaia, notes that Lovelock sees the world and its atmosphere as a self-regulating negative feedback system. Human life is one element in an interacting but unitary organism.[19]

The Anthropic Principle

The key aspect of modern design argument is the Anthropic Principle. Our universe has to take account of our presence. The universe is bigger and older than we ever imagined, and we seem to be an almost totally insignificant part of the whole, and yet physicists tell us that the universe had to be the size and age that it is to make our existence possible. We noted the necessity of the low entropy state; to this is added the nature of the Big Bang, where expansion must be sufficient to overcome gravity, but not so large as to inhibit the development of stars and galaxies; the temperatures involved had to be sufficient for the chemical reactions in the first formed stars that would ultimately lead through super-novae to the distribution of life-forming carbon in that part of the universe where the earth formed.[20]

Fine tuning

Amazingly, tiny changes in many of the fundamental constants of nature in the initial state of the universe would have prevented the existence of atom-based life of any sort. It is this fine tuning that has been one of the most fascinating discoveries of modern science, and which provides a fourth aspect of a modern design argument. With regard to this feature, there are two possible interpretations that we can put forward. On the one hand we can conclude that this is the only possible universe, and that it has been ordered with the purpose of bringing conscious observers into existence. On the other hand it might be argued that this universe is one of many universes, so that although our position is special, we are here by accident.

The mystery of personality

Even for some biologists, the appearance of *Homo sapiens* is a surprise. There is a distinctiveness in personhood.

So we have to ask: what kind of universe can be the context for the evolution of beings such as us? The Anthropic Principle, together with our distinctive personhood, would lead us to raise the possibility of God who is both transcendent as the purposeful creator and immanent as the God of personhood. Yet these scientific arguments have the same fundamental problems as the philosophical arguments of Anselm and Aquinas. They can be pointers to, but not proofs of, the existence of God.

Yet, these researchers are also helping us to understand what sort of God is indicated by the world of nature and of living organisms. We see here a picture of the God of purpose, who works through choices at every stage, who works through the world of quantum physics, of physical laws, and of natural selection. The journey of development we have traced in Part II points us to a God who travels with, and suffers with, his creation. We shall be developing this understanding further in Part III, but for the moment we should note briefly that this suffering can be seen clearly exposed on the evolutionary path; it is seen in the mutations that lead to extinction, in the genetic variations that lead to disorder, as well as in those that lead to an improved life or enhanced reproduction and therefore survival of the species. The God who shares this journey with his creation is the God we find in the Scriptures; he is the God of the cross. This leads Nancey Murphy to describe a nature in which God suffers through its evolution, as 'cross-shaped'.[21]

There are scientific arguments which oppose the conclusions of the Anthropic Principle. Richard Dawkins would take a quite different view from Paul Davies, drawing attention to the nature of chance and uncertainty in the universe in general, and in the evolution of life in particular. While he does not suggest brute chance, his 'tamed chance' is blind. It is the process of natural selection, through non-random survival, that leads to the variety and complexity of life as we know it, including ourselves. If we wish to recognize human beings as the goal of creation, then we must believe that the pathway that nature *did* follow was guided. However, rather than denying chance, we might then try to incorporate it into the design. Polkinghorne[22] attempts to do this, arguing that chance and necessity give a world with ragged edges, where order and disorder are interlaced; chance then leads both to systems of increasing complexity and new possibilities, and also to imperfectly formed, malfunctioning systems. 'Natural evil' is thus seen as a kind of untidiness and disorder. The large question which then arises, however, is whether such a world could be one created in love by a good creator. We note that for Jacques Monod[23] the role of chance simply becomes evidence of meaninglessness in the process of the world, and consequently moves us away from the possibility of a God of purpose.

A further problem with the design argument appears to be the opposite to the challenge of chance. The more we stress design, the more difficult it is for us to keep freedom in view. Consequently, there is a problem with the kind of God that scientific arguments seem to lead to. Scientists have a variety of beliefs, which will be based, at least in part, on the models that they derive from observation and experience of the universe. Science is not necessarily concerned with ultimate truth, and is always ready to accommodate change in the light of new discoveries. The basis of the Christian faith, by contrast, lies in God's revelation of himself and the truths that are formulated in reflection upon this revelation. Cosmologists can look for one super-law, a theory of everything, without reference to God, because all their talk about design is merely an expression of how they observe the universe. Most scientists are certainly not looking to prove or to disprove the existence of God, but simply to understand the universe scientifically. So religious believers (including some scientists) can build a picture of 'God' on scientific models and present him as a divine 'mathematician' or an infinite 'computer programmer'; the resulting defect, from a truly theological point of view, is that a logically consistent universe which is the creation of a supreme mathematician or programmer seems to leave no room for freedom. No freedom means no relationship, and therefore no personal involvement of a personal God.

The place of natural theology in a doctrine of creation

Here then is the problem for the arguments for the existence of God based upon scientific discovery of the natural world: they are equally capable of leading toward a position of no belief, precisely because they are not proofs. Realizing this, Christian thinkers from Calvin to Barth have stressed the need for revelation, as opposed to reason. Their criticism is not just that rational arguments do not work; they make the theological point that our knowledge of a God who is other than us must come from God's own initiative, whereas with natural theology the movement seems to be from us to God. But natural theology takes on a different aspect if we begin from the initiative God takes in coming to meet us in the world.

The Bible presents us with many instances of God encountering people where they are, and in this way our understanding of God through our contemplation of the natural world can be seen as a part of the way in which he reveals himself to us. Knowledge of God and awareness of him is a natural part of our humanity, and may even provide a point of contact for God's special revelation. The apostle Paul was certainly ready to concede this point, as evidenced by his address to the Athenians in the Areopagus (Acts 17), and his statements in Romans 1.18–20 ('God's nature has been visible in the things he has made') and 2.14 ('Gentiles ... do by nature what the law requires').

God does not stand outside of his creation; he is involved with it, sustaining it by his power.[24] God continues with his work; in the imagery of Genesis 1, the seventh day of Genesis 2.1–3 has not brought creation to an end but runs out into history. The Bible affirms order: there is Koheleth's despair that he cannot understand the order that he knows is there,[25] God's opening the mystery of creative order to Job,[26] Yahweh's reassurance through Deutero-Isaiah of his power to bring order,[27] Paul's corrective of the church at Corinth,[28] and Jesus' affirmation that the signs of nature are dependable.[29] The Genesis 1 account of creation is like a hymn of praise, more majestic even than Psalm 104. It is a hymn in the sense that believers down through some 25 centuries or more have found it inspires them to praise the creator. Creation finds its fulfilment in the restored relationship between humanity and God that is focused in Jesus Christ. This is made clear in New Testament passages that pick up the creation theme.[30] We find that all of creation finds its renewal and completion in the final unveiling of the glory of Christ.[31]

The biblical picture is of God's continuous involvement with his creation described in terms of the 'covenant' agreement he initiates and offers. Israel understood the world as God's good creation in the light of her experience of the exodus from Egypt, the Covenant made at Sinai, and entry into the Promised Land. It was from its experience of the life, crucifixion, and resurrection of Christ, and the establishment of the new covenantal community in the power of the Holy Spirit, that the New Testament church understood God's intention to perfect and complete his creation. Thus the natural world is given a place in the whole story of God's purpose to make covenantal fellowship, a process with an eschatological goal. All biblical witness to the creation in which God acts begins from these insights of faith, made in response to what people found to be a revelation of God's purposes. In contrast to a theistic view, biblical natural theology looks to a biblical God, the God of Israel, the Father of Jesus Christ, who is personal and opens himself to all the hazards of love for others. It places God in an immanent, intimate relationship with his creation.

A natural theology which builds a concept of God totally outside the experience of revelation and the community of faith thus belongs to Greek philosophy rather than to Hebrew concepts of the world. While Newton placed God 'out there', somewhere in space, first Darwin and then modern cosmologists and physicists have allowed us to posit an immanent creator, continuously involved with his creation. The Bible has no place for the 'God of the gaps' nor for Newton's God, who set the machine in operation and then sat back and let it run.

The world of modern science with its discoveries and beliefs is a part of the world that we experience in our time. The biblical writers developed their understanding of revealed truths in constant interaction with the beliefs and principles of both their own people and those of neighbouring cultures; and it should not surprise us if modern Christian thought does the same. We bring our understanding of theology to the discoveries of science and allow each to inform the other. So our understanding of the God whom we worship through Christ will be primarily shaped through the revelation we receive by means of Scripture, and tested both through the interpretation of Scripture in the believing community and through scientific investigation of the world.

We have discovered that cosmologists are finding that the dimensions, nature, and age of the universe demonstrate an inbuilt purpose. When it comes to the laws and the initial conditions of the universe we need a fine-tuned high precision that leaves design as a compelling suggestion. We have uncovered a fine-tuned universe that is uniquely suitable for life forms such as ourselves. The question 'How?' of science directs our rational minds to ask 'Why?', a question that belongs to philosophy and theology.

Yet we must take care as we begin to answer this question. Stephen

Hawking suggests that all scientific theories about the universe are only mathematical models existing in the human mind, and as he seeks an answer to the origin of the universe, his 'god' is a super-law of mathematics, the finding of which would be the greatest human achievement.[32] So we have to ask what *sort* of God is implied by our scientific discoveries. We are in danger of positing a rational God who has designed a universe with precision and laws, but who cannot bring about changes in the design of his creation. The creation of such a God would be perfect and rational, with no possibility of choice within it. This is not the God revealed in Scripture. It is difficult to arrive at a picture of the eternal, loving, and self-giving God from the ever changing theories of science. However rational in our perception these theories may be, they do not offer a proof for the existence of God, nor do they point to the God and Father of our Lord Jesus Christ.

There are two fundamental problems with the argument for God's existence from the apparent design of the universe.

i) It is possible to accept the design as a brute fact, with the rider that this universe that we are able to observe is just one of many, and just happens to be the one that by chance has the characteristics needed for our evolution.

ii) A God who is the originator or designer of the universe need in no way have the character of the Christian God of love. Although the modern arguments for design are far stronger than those of Anselm and Aquinas, they still have the same inherent problems. John Hick[33] is right to draw a number of conclusions.

   a) The argument from design does not establish divine existence, but poses the question to which one answer can be God.

   b) One cannot suggest that the existence of an eternal creative Mind is self-explanatory, while a universe that exhibits the fundamental laws it does exhibit, is not.

   c) While we all perceive the physical world around us, our beliefs about that world will depend on the information and experience available to us. For a Christian, belief in a purposeful creator is seen to be completely reasonable in the light of scientific research, but for a non-Christian there may be other explanations for the nature of the universe.

The conclusions of scientists like Paul Davies,[34] who take no account of revelation or religious experience, will take us no further than some power or force, a kind of demiurge, behind the universe. Scientists are likely to avoid the theological implications of their conclusions, and so will not recognize the ways in which human sinfulness will prejudice their views. Basing a religious belief mainly on science can therefore lead to an anthropocentric view of God who, having been discovered as the author of life, is reduced to a being or mind just like us. There can also emerge a deist view that sees God as the distant origin of nature or natural laws, rather than God who is intimately involved with his creation. Nor should we forget that scientific views change, and rapidly become out of date. Cosmology can only be a pointer toward a deeper theological inquiry and understanding, which must be based on the present and historical experience of the community of faith. Jaki quotes an important observation by James Clerk Maxwell (who discovered electromagnetism), when asked to use his scientific discoveries to support an interpretation of Genesis 1:

> I should be very sorry if an interpretation founded on a most conjectural scientific hypothesis were to get fastened to the text in Genesis, even if by so doing it got rid of the old statement of the commentators which has long ceased to be intelligible. The rate of change of scientific hypothesis is naturally much more rapid than that of biblical interpretations, so that if an interpretation is founded on such an hypothesis, it may help to keep the hypothesis above ground long after it ought to be buried and forgotten.[35]

Theological reflection

A universe with a beginning and an end, and design and purpose recognized in the Anthropic Principle, must entail a change in world-view. Add to this the unpredictability within physical processes and the guiding mechanism that is required in the evolution of life, and we recognize a universe that is contingent and not necessary. We have a paradigm shift in our view of the world. The universe is not infinite, nor closed, nor entirely predictable. It has purpose, it is open to change, and so there is a place for faith to find God's immanence as well as his transcendence. Human beings cannot be viewed as machines, as science has recognized the non-algorithmic nature of the mind and of personhood; there are perceptions that are not computable; and the universe seems to have evolved with humankind having a central place. We must therefore question how we obtain information and knowledge, and we cannot see our own individualistic rights and needs as an end in themselves, because we appear to be a part of a cosmic plan. In short, in the modern scientific view of the world there is a place for the mystical, for a God who accompanies creation.

But one of the main problems with God as cosmic designer is the presence of evil in the world that cannot be laid at the door of human beings. Ruth Page is instructive at this point in her quotation of Emil Brunner's question:

> For the more fully we ascribe – in our doctrine of creation – responsibility to God for that which is created, the more disturbing is our view of the actual reality. Can this world, so full of meaningless, cruel, suffering and death – be God's creation?[36]

The church has largely ignored disorder. The emphasis on order has never reflected on chaotic systems, on change as well as stability. This leads Page to state that 'the tidy kind of God discovered in order is not the one who would seem to be able to enjoy diversity and change, or share in the suffering brought about by disorder.'[37]

We have moved away from Newton's determinism to recognize the possibilities at sub-atomic level of a quantum world, and within the evolution of plant and animal life. Of the latter Karl Popper wrote:

> It is obvious in the case of the evolution of life that the future was always open. It is obvious that in the evolution of life there were almost infinite possibilities. But they were largely exclusive possibilities.[38]

By 'exclusive', Popper recognizes that the occurrence of one life form, especially if it were advantageously adapted, could exclude other possibilities. Yet as a result other possibilities may be opened up. To those who are unhappy with the openness of such possibilities we might ask the question raised by J. B. Phillips: 'Is your God too small?'[39] Do we by our insistence on laws and order, design and certainty, simply look for a God who is under control – and our control at that?

Page believes in a God who is not responsible for order or disorder, but 'freely made it possible for creation to come into being, shaping and reshaping the world in the process ... Some of the outcomes of God's free creation undoubtedly cause grief and suffering to other creatures. One cannot draw an optimistic picture of universal well-being or cooperation.'[40] Freedom gives opportunity for love by, and relationship to, a God of love.

So we come to ask, 'What sort of God?' We discovered in our study of Genesis 1 that that account of creation presents or prompts important doctrinal statements concerning God's relationship with his creation. We note that the ordering of creation depicted is at least consistent with cosmological and geological histories of the universe. But there are no proofs to be found here, for while modern cosmology presents a picture of purpose and fulfilment, faith takes us beyond this to see God's promise and fulfilment. Science may point us towards the God question, but it is faith that leads us to a personal God, revealed in Jesus Christ. Jesus Christ is not only the agent of creation, he is also the agent of salvation, fulfilling God's personal promise to heal relationships.

We recognize the broader, holistic view, suggested by modern cosmology and significantly, also, recorded far earlier in Scripture, that the universe demonstrates design and purpose, which reflects the mind of God. A world which displays both autonomy and contingency discloses the character of God, and the experience of people down through the ages, recorded in the Scriptures, witnesses to God's self-limiting love which gives freedom and looks for response.

The model of creation that we are proposing is neither the pantheistic model of paganism, nor the panentheistic model of process thought and some green theologies, but rather it is a Christian trinitarian model.

The biblical model of 'making' stresses transcendence – the difference between God and creatures; it represents creation as a free act on the part of God. The model introduced by early theologians such as Origen is of emanation, which suggests the immanence of God; it suggests an affinity and even closeness between the source and that which has sprung from it, but does not suggest that creatures are like in substance to the creator. It avoids, according to Macquarrie, the impression that creation might be an arbitrary act, but runs the danger of leaving the view that it is a natural process.[41] Macquarrie believes that the insights of both the biblical and early church models should be combined, so that the transcendent letting-be is combined with immanent involvement of God – the risk of creation that really matters to him. Keith Ward helpfully expresses this relationship with reference to the trinity:

> The idea of God as Trinity emerges with the thought that God, as the creator and Father of the universe, the only source of its being, is also the Spirit who enters into created, alienated being to reconcile it to the divine life. This God, utterly transcendent in creative power and utterly immanent in reconciling love, takes particular and paradigmatic form in a human life ... As the Spirit reconciles creation to the Father, it transforms created being into participation in the divine. In Jesus, this

transformation is effected fully in a human life, and the at-one-ment of alienated creation and perfect Creator is realised.[42]

The christological centre of the Christian faith is foreshadowed in our discussion of creation, where the transcendent-immanent relation between expressive Being and beings is already to be found. The Spirit is seen moving over the waters. Paul speaks of creation groaning as it awaits the fruit of the Spirit in human beings. This leads Macquarrie to observe:

> Here we have the picture of the Spirit, as unitive Being, lifting the whole creation toward God, bringing the beings into a reconciling unity with Being, yet without destroying their diversity.[43]

The Incarnation speaks of God's deepest possible involvement with creation; the Resurrection is the hope of a destiny for all creation; the Ascension is the possibility of being caught up in eternity with God; and Pentecost marks out God's continuing involvement with his world now, with the possibility of new creation. The Spirit works through the whole of creation – it is the whole of creation that groans.

7 Letting the Stories be Heard – Listening to Each Other

For since the creation of the world God's invisible qualities – his eternal power and divine nature – have been clearly seen, being understood from what has been made . . .[1]

Modern scientific discoveries are providing us with many answers to our questions about the nature of life and about the universe, but the question of ultimate meaning remains a problem. We will need to recognize at the outset that there is a limit to how far science can ever take us in our understanding of the world in which we live. The former NASA astrophysicist, Robert Jastrow, was probably correct in his assessment:

> For the scientist who has lived by his faith in the power of reason, the story ends like a bad dream. He has scaled the mountains of ignorance; he is about to conquer the highest peak; and as he pulls himself over the final rock, he is greeted by a band of theologians who have been sitting there for centuries.[2]

We need to recognize the close historic and logical connection between the theistic doctrine of creation and the enterprise of science and technology. The conflicts between scientists and organized religion, as we have seen, were occasional, partly accidental and often involved clashes of personalities. Many scientists saw their work as studying 'Nature's book' or 'thinking God's thoughts after him'; as the modern cosmologist George Smoot says at the end of his account of the search for the origin of the universe:

> The religious concept of creation flows from a sense of wonder at the existence of the universe and our place in it. The scientific concept of creation encompasses no less a sense of wonder: we are awed by the ultimate simplicity and power of the creativity of physical nature – and by its beauty on all scales.[3]

However, scientific failures and dangers, environmental problems and disasters point to the need for ethical concern and consideration. Stewardship, in a Christian perspective, sees human beings being responsible to God for the ways in which the earth is used and preserved. We will discuss this further in the next chapter.

There are advantages to be gained through dialogues between science and religion. Science is concerned with reality, and it is important to understand and examine the world in which we live; but it is also important to recognize that there are questions which science cannot answer. We discover that there are questions that are answered by research and by reference to the component parts that make up the stuff of life and the universe; but there are also questions that can only be answered at a higher level, what Nancey Murphy has referred to as 'boundary questions'.[4] Some of the most fundamental boundary questions can be answered by theology; for example, questions of meaning and purpose. Thus, we attempt to make sense of the stories of science and religion. Howard Snyder draws attention to the paradox, found in postmodernism, of fragmentation and integration. Fragmentation appears in family life and old ideologies; yet there is integration in increasing global connections, growing environmental consciousness, fresh forms of community, expanding communications networks, and new proposals in science for a Theory of Everything. He correctly observes that 'such paradoxes signal an old order dying and a new, uncertain age aborning'.[5] He then proceeds to identify some of the fundamental questions to be addressed: what key trends will shape our lives over the next 30 years? what are the main dangers we face? what are the signs of hope? where will truth and meaning come from? Is there meaning? what are the options for hope and faith? what about God – within us, out there, between us, gone? Is a coherent life and worldview possible today?[6] These are the areas we shall seek to address in the concluding chapters of this book.

Where have the discoveries of science led us?

As we approach the end of the millennium, new observations and new theories in cosmology are extending our understanding of the universe in amazing ways, as we build on a long history of scientific discovery. Scientific research over the last couple of centuries has seen an enormous expansion, which continues to grow ever larger. Stephen Hawking remarked, 'A lot of (Nobel) prizes have been awarded for showing that the universe is not as simple as we might have thought.'[7] John Barrow, who professes no specific beliefs, describes how science has always looked for a theory that would explain the whole of our knowledge of the universe. He notes[8] that the early Greeks, with a teleological perspective on the world of living things, saw the world as a great organism. But for those who developed geometry, the universe was seen as a geometric harmony. When clockwork, the pendulum, and Newton's mathematics were the basis of science, a cosmic clockmaker was sought. With the industrial revolution and thermodynamics, the universe was pictured as a giant heat engine. Today some scientists liken the universe to a computer. Barrow enquires, 'What will the next paradigm be?'[9] These successive models show that for many hundreds (if not thousands) of years scientists have been impressed by the intelligibility and comprehensibility of the natural world, together with its apparently rational nature.

Science is essentially involved in a rational exploration of the universe; it is a search for understanding of the nature and patterns of the physical world. Science is only effective because it describes things the way they are. The discovery of the physical laws, such as gravity, that govern the universe, are part of objective reality; they are objective truth and not the invention or imagining of some scientist. The whole field of science is one of discovery and not construction; there is an honesty and integrity in the search for meaning.

Scientific results are frequently cross-checked and validated or questioned when other workers repeat the same experiments.

But there are, of course, the spectacles of a scientific worldview, which will include various presuppositions and theories. This will mean that all facts are, to a greater or lesser extent, interpreted facts. There will be both the personal commitment of the scientists in their search for truth, and the personal judgement of the individual researcher.[10]

This scientific witness to comprehensibility is, however, ambiguous. While scientists may use theistic language as a means of denoting this basic character of the universe, we must not assume that they are inferring a personal God who is intimately involved with his creation, and is looking for a response from it. Scientists and theologians may use similar words whilst giving them different values and meanings. This is seen in the writings of Paul Davies and Stephen Hawking, who both use 'God' language in describing the origin and evolution of the universe.

When the wrinkles in the background radiation field were finally mapped out, Smoot[11] was able to confirm that the Big Bang origin of the universe was correct, and that the pattern of the wrinkles was about right to yield the major structures of today's universe, under gravitational collapse through 15 billion years. Cosmology – through the marriage of astrophysics and particle physics – is showing us that this complex universe began from a deep simplicity. We get back to a situation of the infinitely small point of energy – creation from practically nothing but not nothing. There is a temptation for theologians at this point to draw comparisons with Genesis 1.1, a temptation made all the more attractive by the concept of the Anthropic Principle. The weak anthropic principle is essentially tautology: it says that a world in which human beings are found is the result of a universe that had the conditions in which human beings might evolve. But the strong form sees human beings as the central purpose of the universe, and emphasizes the fine-tuned nature of its initial conditions. A number of scientists would dispute such an anthropocentric view of the universe. Richard Dawkins and Stephen Jay Gould would see the presence of human beings as one chance among many in the evolution of life.[12]

The quest of modern cosmology for a 'theory of everything' may be understood as a search for the cause behind the Big Bang. There is a wistful belief that if only one could find the equation that brought all the factors together, the law by which the other laws work, one would be able to explain how the Big Bang happened. John Barrow, although not holding a particular religious belief, helps us with the central theological issue. He considers the three basic factors of God, the universe, and the laws of nature, and then draws up three groups of parallel propositions:

i) *Either* the laws of nature existed before the universe (a 'first cause'); *or* the laws are dependent on the universe; *or* the laws are to be equated with the universe.

ii) A similar set of propositions can be made with regard to God: *either* the universe is part of God ('panentheism' – everything in God); *or* God is part of the universe (a creation of the human mind); *or* God is the same as the universe ('pantheism').

iii) Again, a third set of propositions might be: *either* the laws of nature are part of God; *or* God is part of the laws of nature; *or* the laws of nature are the same as God.[13]

There is, of course, no logical necessity for coming to the conclusion that the universe points to the God of the Christian Scriptures, but there is an interesting affinity between the first of these propositions in each set, and a potential here for a 'suggestive' natural theology.

However, we might suggest that a God of personal relationships could be argued to be a more convincing explanation for all the features of the universe, including consciousness, than a super-law or mere 'theory of everything' would be. But we must underline once again that we are not dealing with a proof here. John Hick is right to complain that advocates of a cosmological argument too easily suppose that any reasonable person *must* agree that the existence of an eternal creative Mind would be self-explanatory in a way in which the existence of the physical universe, exhibiting the fundamental laws which it does exhibit, would not.[14] In this respect Paul Davies is right to point out that the design of the universe is a fact, but that belief in a designer is 'a matter of personal taste'; this would apply equally to an argument from cause. Because of the rational way in which our minds operate, we see the universe as needing explanation. This need grows stronger when we picture a universe that begins in a Big Bang explosion, as this means that we are able to conceive of a universe that might have been different; that is, it is 'contingent'. It makes sense then, as we consider the 'fine tuning' of the universe, to think of a creative divine Mind behind the universe. Yet having reached such a point in the argument, Bertrand Russell's conclusion is still open to us as a logical possibility; namely, there is the explanation of brute fact, that the universe is just there and that is all. The cosmological argument, like the argument from design, points to the possibility of God, but does not provide a proof of his existence.

We can conclude by recognizing that science has a number of things to say to theology. i) Physics does not allow us to build metaphysical models. ii) Science will not allow us to go beyond our understanding. iii) The history of the universe is pointing to a God who does not work by magic, but who has been patiently at work, over a long period of time, in an evolving universe. There is a picture of the outworking of divine love here, which we will have to consider in some detail. Science reveals an interplay of chance and necessity within the evolution of the universe, which points us toward another aspect of divine love, namely, freedom. iv) Science presents us with a universe that has a beginning and which will have a definite end, in which carbon-based life will be extinguished. v) Lastly, it is the human mind that is able to observe, investigate and understand the world that we experience. Scientific research has demonstrated that the mind does not function like a computer.[15] It may be possible to reduce everything else to sub-atomic particles, acting under the laws of physics, but there are aspects of the mind, namely those of personhood, which do not compute. Once more we are pointed toward the possibility of God.

What have our biblical investigations revealed?

Despite its variety of writings, the Bible offers a coherent worldview; God not only is allowed a place in it, but it is explicitly orientated around him, and we need to understand how this worldview came about. We have already recognized that the writers of the biblical accounts of creation were influenced by their understanding of the world that they experienced, by the mythological stories and liturgical practices of the peoples around, and also by their own religious experiences including the revelation of their covenant God, who was intimately involved in their history. These revelations were within their own particular culture and understanding of the world. Thus their perception of the world is both objective and subjective. The cultural influences need to be recognized – the Old Testament arose within a nomadic, agrarian culture, while the New Testament is influenced by both Greek and Roman culture in addition to its Jewish milieu.

From a biblical perspective, God is identified with power, holiness, and love. The creator is distinguished from his creation. God is transcendent, beyond human intellect, and yet is not outside of creation. The personhood of God is understood as love, which is further explored in the form of triune relationships within God by the early church as it reflected on the biblical witness. Creation is seen as good, but evil emerges within creation as a result of the freedom with which God, in self-limiting love, endowed the world. Human beings are affirmed as being in the image of God,[16] and as such are able to think, reason, discover, and exercise control over their surroundings; nevertheless, full understanding lies beyond this world.[17] Human life is God-breathed life;[18] while humanity has a solidarity with the rest of creation, it is seen to be distinct from it, and in the image of God to have an exceptional freedom to make choices and to love. Choices include ethical decision-making, which is guided by the moral standard of the creator's revealed character.

In our consideration of the creation narratives of Genesis, and other passages within Scripture that reflect on the nature of the physical world, we have recognized that they represent the reflections of a community of faith. The priestly writers of Genesis 1 reflected upon the nature of the universe that they experienced, and the beliefs of the other religions around them, in the light of their own experience of God's self-revelation, and that of the whole religious community of which they were a part. We have understood that those reflections must have been consistent with the reality both of their experiences of the physical world and of their spiritual experiences of God.

In our time, when we seek to interpret these passages we must do so recognizing the way in which they originated, and in the light of our own experience both of the world and of the faith of the believing community of which we are a part. The Bible points to God as the source of order, and as intimately involved with his creation. The supremely exciting contribution that theology makes is the insight that God makes himself known in Jesus Christ. The Genesis account of creation shows us that God has put relationship at the heart of the universe. Human beings are created in the image of God, to care for creation, and to worship their creator. God is seen to be in dynamic relationship with his creation. This comes into clear focus in Jesus Christ, where the divine takes human flesh and shares our life. The social sciences have recognized a human longing for ultimate reality; this longing finds its rest in the Christ of the gospel, and the resurrection of Christ is the ground, foretaste and guarantee of life beyond death. Here is the disclosure of ultimate reality and purpose for humankind.

Theology addresses science in a number of places.

1. First of all, while science deals with the minutiae of particles or the mega theories of the universe, theology attempts to pull the whole of human experience, physical, mental, emotional and spiritual, together, producing a holistic view of the universe in which we exist.
2. Secondly, theology is able to bring answers to the questions that science is posing. Theology hears the questions raised by the fine-tuning of the universe and the Anthropic Principle, and sees within these the hand of God described at the beginning of Scripture.
3. Lastly, theology is able to speak of nothing lying outside of the will of God, and is able to bring together the purpose of the universe, the meaning of life, and the question of what lies beyond death, or beyond the end of the universe's life. Theology brings together those issues that affect both science and itself. Because the theological view of the world is a total all-embracing view, Polkinghorne is right to conclude that there must be a consonance between science and theology.[19]

The picture of God that is developing

First of all, the Bible presents us with God's ordering of creation. Westermann points out the repeated pattern of Genesis 1 in the words:

Introduction	And God said
Command	Let it be
Completion	And it was so
Judgement	And God saw that it was good
Time sequence	And it was evening[20]

In creating, God enters time, so time is an expression of the action of God. The universe with all its parts is not suddenly brought into being in one mighty act; it is created in an orderly fashion: time and space; the world and the heavens; land and sea; the animate and inanimate; and human beings. All is laid out in the pattern of one week, ending with the sabbath worship. However, there is no need for us to be restricted to the theological meaning that emerges from taking the seven days in their strict chronological order. Taking the week as a whole is a picture of unity, but we may then view it from another perspective; we may see the first three days as setting the broad canvas for creation, and the second three days as filling in the finer detail of created things. The first day reveals how light came into existence, and the fourth the sources and purposes of light. The second day explains how the atmosphere came into existence, separating the waters below from those above, and the fifth day details the life in the waters and the life in the atmosphere. The third day relates the emergence of dry land and the establishment of vegetation, while the sixth day deals with the population of the land by animals and human beings, who together depend on the vegetation for their sustenance. There is an order here that can be related to the cosmological and geological history of earth, as I have shown else-where.[21] Studies in ecology add connectedness to order. They suggest two key characteristics of the earth: its unity (wholeness) and its diversity (distinction), with meaning arising from the relationship between the parts. The patterns and linkages of the universe are suggestive of fundamental meaning, although connectedness does not prove mean-ing. Meaning comes from the perception of a transcendent reality; faith in a personal God.

Second, the Bible shows us God's covenantal relationship with creation.[22] God cares about the world that he has made. He has not only been involved in its shaping, he is intimately involved in the lives of its creatures. He has given creation freedom and as a result lives with the consequences of self-willed beings. The new covenant after the Flood reminds us that such freedom brings grief to the creator, and that we are always looking from the side of a broken creation. God, for his part, promises the faithfulness of seasons and harvests, but there is also the human side of the covenant. The priestly writers raise questions about human relationships; the relationships of creatures towards one another; the slaughter of animals; and violence inflicted by human beings on one another. The human side is through a relationship with God in worship, and a caring relationship with nature.

But we find that paradise is lost; creation is broken, constantly in need of restoration. The third biblical aspect to consider is redemption. It is not only human beings who suffer in such a fallen world; the biosphere that is becoming increasingly polluted and exhausted also suffers. As Paul wrote to the church at Rome:

> The creation waits in eager expectation for the children of God to be revealed ... We know that the whole creation has been groaning as in the pains of childbirth right up to the present time. Not only so, but we ourselves, who have the firstfruits of the Spirit, groan inwardly as we wait eagerly for our adoption, the redemption of our bodies.[23]

We live in a world of suffering, pain, pollution, and exploitation, but our hope is in transformation of individuals and through them of creation, in Christ crucified, resurrected and ascended. As Paul challenges, for creation to be redeemed requires the first step of human beings becoming truly human, that is, *imago Dei*. But in a broken world, fulfilment of this vision awaits the coming of Christ in glory, at the end of time.

Putting science and faith together

The theological view of the world is a holistic (physical and spiritual) view and so there must be an agreement between science and theology, if both pictures of the universe are correct. Understanding the world in which we live is a quest that unites science and theology, and such a quest will require an openness to God, Scripture, and scientific research. The world is not a neutral place and, if it is the creation of God, we should expect a study of the universe to be a starting point for recognizing the creator.

Some might question whether it is possible to bring together the fields of science and theology; are they too disparate? and do they not speak different languages and use different methodology? If we believe that God is the creator of the whole of life, the universe and everything, then we must see his involvement in the domain of scientific research, and not merely confine God-talk to the church and seminary. Lesslie Newbigin has rightly attacked the division between the public world of scientific facts and the private world of beliefs and values.[24] Scientists have their own beliefs, doubts, questions, and certainties; and the world of public decision making clearly needs the values, ethics, morality, and perspective that an understanding of the Christian faith might bring to it.

Both theology and science are seeking to make sense of the world that they experience, and their methodologies are not totally different. In each case the search for a rational understanding is motivated by belief and a desire for truth. As such there must be a common ground for dialogue. Science is able to investigate the universe because human beings have a measure of transcendence over the world, and theology is able to bring a greater degree of understanding because it recognizes the transcendence of God, who reveals his purposes to humankind. Understanding the world in which we live is an undertaking that unites science and theology, and the search for truth will not succeed without a commitment to belief and a readiness for testing, confirmation, and correction. However, we need to recognize that it is at the philosophical level, rather than the technological level, that such dialogue might take place. We may want answers to the 'how' of creation but the biblical writers are concerned with something else. They proclaim something of the unsearchable mystery of God. We mistake the purpose of, for example, Genesis 1, if we expect it to answer the questions that we, with the benefit of modern science, ask about creation. The Scriptures are the writings of a faith community, and we recognize that faith moves beyond empirical knowledge.

We live between the beginning and the end, with no knowledge of either, although the Bible speaks about both. It begins with God's revelation that he is the one who creates and who is not remote, but eternally present and related to his creation. The Bible declares that the end will be God's consummation of the universe, the taking of the whole of creation back into God. We can only know of the beginning as we hear of it in the middle between beginning and end. No question can penetrate behind the beginning; for Stephen Hawking it is the ultimate frustration – he cannot get behind or before the Big Bang. Dietrich

Bonhoeffer considers that this free event of the beginning is unique – 'the Creator, in freedom, creates the creature ... their connexion is not conditioned ... Creator and creature cannot be said to have a relation of cause and effect, for between Creator and creature there is neither a law of motive nor a law of effect.'[25] Creation is out of a void, in and through which freedom operates, but the resurrection tells us that God will be in the end.

From the beginning, the biblical picture is of God's continuous risky involvement with his creation described in terms of the freedom he grants, and 'covenant' agreement he initiates and offers. Israel understood the world as God's good creation in the light of her experience of the exodus from Egypt, the Covenant made at Sinai, and entry into the Promised Land. It was from its experience of the life, crucifixion, and resurrection of Christ, and the establishment of the new covenantal community in the power of the Holy Spirit, that the New Testament church understood God's intention to perfect and complete his creation. Thus the natural world is given a place in the whole story of God's purpose to make covenantal fellowship, a process with an eschatological goal. All biblical witness to the creation in which God acts begins from these insights of faith, made in response to what people found to be a revelation of God's purposes.

John Hick has suggested that the risk God takes in creation can be understood as his creating human persons at a 'distance' from himself, to give room for genuine response rather than being overwhelmed by his glory.[26] Paul Fiddes takes up this idea, extending it to all levels of nature, and suggesting that God thereby freely exposes himself to whatever new things, alien to his purposes, might emerge from the choices of an unresponsive creation.[27] He further proposes that this risk can be pictured in the symbol of 'non-being'. The making of creatures 'from nothing' (*ex nihilo*) means that as finite beings they will always be limited by non-being, as a boundary to life which is typified by death. While this 'non-being' is neutral in itself, the freedom that God has granted to creation leads to an environment in which a lapsing toward hostile non-being is practically inevitable. That is, the human 'no' to God (sin) results in an aggressive and alienating power that wants to reduce personal life and relationships to nothingness.[28]

In creation 'from nothing', therefore, God exposes himself to a 'non-being' which begins as a natural boundary to life and which becomes increasingly hostile and alien to him. It is possible to represent this diagrammatically, as shown in Figure 2. Alongside this theological statement, and interacting with it, we can place the Big Bang of cosmology through which God creates our universe with its fine tuning, and through whose evolution we see the development of self-conscious human beings. We have a whole series of arrows, all of which are pointing in the direction of the space-time arrow, but which represent the contrasting movements of development and disorder.

There is the arrow of evolution, giving an increasing complexity and variety of life forms within an 'open system'; but paired with this arrow of development is that of disorder as entropy increases and the cosmos heads towards the Big Crunch or Heat Death. Parallel to these cosmic movements is the arrow of sin leading towards hostile non-being, paired with the arrow of redemption as God continuously participates in his creation to seek to draw it back to himself.

We should notice that the 'theological' and 'scientific' beginnings are not exactly simultaneous, as we cannot know whether God's initial act of creation is identical with the creation of this universe. So also the end-points are not coterminous, as God's consummation of the universe is at his initiative and not a matter of scientific prediction. We also need to recognize that from a theological standpoint all these arrow-lines are transfigured by one defining moment, when God participates in his creation in the deepest possible way through his incarnation in Christ. As Jüngel says, 'In the death of Jesus Christ God's "Yes" which constitutes all being, exposed itself to the "No" of the nothing ... and in the Resurrection, this "Yes" prevailed over the "No".'[29] So there is the possibility of humans being taken out of the descent to hostile non-being and being caught up in the Being of God who is on his way to his goal of new creation. Through cross and resurrection the arrow of redemption ends in resurrection and renewal for the whole cosmos.

Figure 2 puts in picture form the mutual witness of science and faith that I have been exploring in this section. It also expresses the complex relation between evolutionary progress and entropic decline in a scientific cosmology, which parallels the complex relation between fallenness and redemption in a Christian view of the world. It is not possible in a scientific perspective to make the neat distinction between entropy at a level of individual systems and openness at the level of the *whole* system of the universe. Nor are the arrow-lines of movement according to science and theology simply analogous; there is a real interaction between them which we have only begun to explore here.

Another feature of complexity here belongs to God's goal in creation and redemption. On the one hand, according to the New Testament,

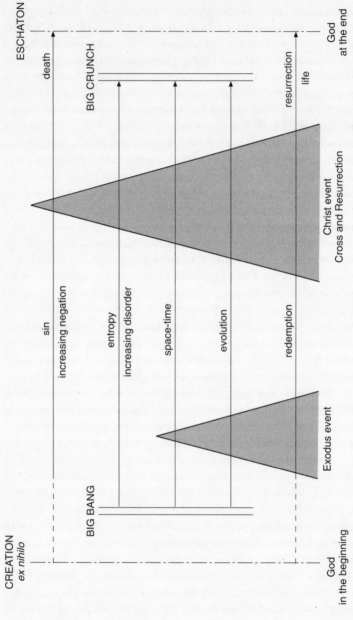

Figure 2. A model for the relationship between a theological view and a scientific view of the evolving universe

God is sure to bring about a perfected creation, which celebrates his glory, and brings forth joy and thanksgiving and praise from every living thing. This is seen as the ultimate deliverance of creation from frustration and suffering into the freedom and bliss of God.[30] It is the final working out of the goal of creation set out in Genesis 2.1–3, and can be seen as the fulfilment of the Anthropic Principle suggested by modern cosmology. But at the same time, the arrow-line of human development allows for real freedom in making choices and selecting possibilities; so we must ask whether the end is fixed or a risk.

Here I think that Fiddes is right to draw our attention to the nature of God's project in making persons. He suggests that when we are dealing with persons, we cannot separate the road from the destination.[31] He proposes, then, that the risk upon which God has embarked is real and serious, though not a total one. God has a certain hope in the *fact* of the end, which shifts creation onto an altogether new level of existence; but there is a genuine openness about the route and therefore the *content* of the end, which is the nature of the persons who are being reconciled. So there is room for tragedy as well as for triumph in God's victory over suffering. In the final vision of God the worshippers will not be disappointed, but God knows that they may not have reached their full potential.

There are moments of special definition within the experience of God's people, which were and are looked back upon as exceptional; these are represented by shaded segments in Figure 2. It is a reasonable historical claim that some events happened at the time of Israel's leaving slavery in Egypt that were understood as exceptional by those who participated in them. Faith can perceive God's special revelation of himself occurring in the normal events of the physical world; for example, there was the strong wind blowing back the waters of the Sea of Reeds,[32] and the resulting destruction as the tide swept back in, creating the kind of tragedy that frequently occurs on coastal mud-flats in the UK, such as Morecambe Bay, though on a massive scale. The miracle is seen with the eye of faith; it is belief and faith in God who acts for deliverance. It is possible that here we have an instance of divine intervention, bringing about a combination of tides and winds at just the right time in a way that may have broken through the regularity of natural laws; but the point of the event is revelation – through it the people discover who God is, and they also discover who they are in his creation. God is the God who saves; and they are the people whom he saves. For Christians, our supreme moment of definition and revelation is found on a cross on a hillside outside Jerusalem, and an empty tomb a couple of days later. Here we discover the God who saves, and that we are people whom he saves.

But these events are not proof; they must be apprehended by faith. This salvation is a process, and as such includes our vulnerability as well as God's risk. In Exodus 14.8 we find the vulnerability of the 'cloud', where God places himself between the Israelites and the Egyptians, which is followed by the power of the parting of the sea. In the Passion narratives we see the vulnerability of the Cross, where God places himself between us and hostile non-being, which is followed by the power of the resurrection.

God reveals his transcendence and his immanence in his creation. Cosmology is helping us to understand the magnitude, majesty, and careful purpose that is to be found in the universe, and so helps us to understand more about the power and care of God. Geology and biology are helping us to see the evolutionary path that has culminated in the presence of conscious human beings, and help us to recognize the God who has journeyed with his creation. In the 'disasters' of exploding stars, earthquakes, volcanoes, storms, and mutated plants and animals we have seen something of the suffering that is involved. We have recognized that the suffering of the world is a demonstration of God's self-giving love that takes risks in giving freedom to creation. As we said earlier, this leads Nancey Murphy to describe nature itself as cross-shaped. We recognize that we are created in the image of God; we have been called into a relationship with the creator, with a task to be undertaken and a destiny within his purpose. I warm to the way in which David Atkinson describes this: 'while it is proper to speak of Jesus Christ as the true Human Being, we should speak of ourselves as Human Becomings'.[33]

The recent scientific research into the origin, nature, and evolution of the universe, and of the nature and place of *Homo sapiens* within it, add a great deal of support to the reasonableness of belief. But, however appealing attempts to reconcile Genesis and science are, we should recognize that they can be misleading. They not only have the tendency to gloss over many inconsistencies, but also fail to understand the purpose of Genesis, which is to express something of the relationship of the creator with creation, rather than to give a scientific account of the evolution of the universe. It is also worth restating that we do not know when the next paradigm shift in scientific understanding may occur.

The reasonableness of belief will depend on understanding and experience. A perfect proof of God's existence would not necessarily produce anything more than mental assent; in fact Hick[34] is right to conclude that for many people such a proof would have little effect. Our beliefs are affected by our experiences, and change in the light of these. If we were to argue from human experience, we might suggest that for Christians the step of faith has resulted in a describable experience of God, which confirms their faith. This is God's self-revelation to the individual believer.

Some theological implications

Hearing the scientific stories challenges us to recognize that any theological reflection on creation today, if it is to remain relevant, must not lose sight of the pain of the earth, or forget the forces which are destroying it, by flying off into an abstract discussion on creation and creaturehood. At the same time, a discussion of scientific models of creation would be the poorer if it did not situate a 'state of the earth today' discussion within a broader philosophical context.

The important question that will underlie our reflection is, what sort of God do we believe in? There are a variety of myths in ancient cultures, some of which are nature denying and some of which emphasize its importance in the scheme of things. Enlightenment science has led to views that are at best deist (God winding up the clockwork motor of a world that runs according to physical laws) and at worst reductionist, with no place for the divine.

When we consider the nature of the earth's crust and its weather systems, we recognize an important theological issue. In 1755, an earthquake off the coast of Portugal caused a tidal wave which destroyed much of the port of Lisbon; hundreds of people lost their lives. The Lisbon earthquake is cited by many people as a turning point for belief in a loving, sovereign God. But we now know the structure of the earth's crust; we can predict where earthquakes are likely to occur; and we know that the evolving structure of the crust is necessary for the development of the rocks and minerals on which much of our industrial development is based. We know what causes climatic change and we can predict weather patterns. What will we say when a major earthquake occurs along the San Andreas Fault in California? It surely could not be used as an objection to belief in a God, who is intimately involved with his creation, and who has provided humanity with the materials for an industrialized society through such structures in the earth's crust.

113

Theology seeks to make sense of the universe, but in this is confronted by suffering and evil. We are forced to face not only questions about earthquakes and cyclones, but also questions such as whether a creation that includes a Holocaust or a Bosnia demonstrates the work of a loving God. Suffering presents us with a mystery, but Christianity meets this mystery at the profoundest level in the Cross of Christ. It is here that God involves himself in the suffering of the world. We understand the immanent suffering of God, feeling pain in his relationship with his creation which is in the mixed condition of progress and decline. That God suffers is undeniable, and that God is fulfilled (in some way) through creation must also be true, but this does not imply that God is changed in his inner being by creation. We might consider the analogy that Fiddes employs, between God and a creative artist who sets out with the desire to paint a picture.[35] The artist has the possibility of the finished work in his mind, but the actual painting has new elements within it, which come about as he plays with the materials at his disposal – a variety of brushes, textures, and paints. So God uses the materials of free personalities, from whom he looks for a response in achieving his purposes. This analogy shows that while the picture may change, the divine artist himself remains essentially unchanged, with the exception of the pain that comes with disappointment in those who fail to respond to his love.

Nancey Murphy seeks to reconcile theology with the sciences, drawing on the works of John Howard Yoder and James McClendon, to support the view that Scripture finds its authority in the context of its being read and applied by a community of believing people. She notes that McClendon emphasizes God's faithful, costly, and redemptive love in nature and the whole human story. This allows her to draw her higher level of explanation model to a helpful conclusion. She believes that the late modern world offers the scholar three sealed compartments: the sciences, the moral sphere, and the religious sphere. She claims that these three should be related to each other. 'Without God's revelation in Jesus, we have no way of knowing what is the ultimate purpose of human life, or what are the highest goods human beings can reasonably strive to attain.'[36] Each of the sciences has its own boundary questions, which require an answer at a higher level. Murphy is able to demonstrate that such boundary questions might reasonably be answered through the Christian understanding of the loving creator God, who suffers with his creation, and who has revealed himself to us in Jesus Christ.

In the Christian tradition, philosophers and theologians have dealt with this issue of meaning and relationship in part through the doctrine of the Trinity. As Sean McDonagh affirms: 'The unity – perhaps the meaning – of God is found in the indivisible, ever-intercommunicating relationship of one-in-two, two-in-three, three-in-one. In the Christian view, meaning is therefore trinitarian and relational.'[37] This relationship encompasses the beginning and end of this universe, and indeed is beyond its history.

8 *A Theology for Earthkeeping*

The LORD God took the man and put him in the Garden of Eden to work it and take care of it.[1]

Decreation (The Big Bang Theory)
On the eighth day our rest was disturbed
by the drumming of machinery;
pistons pumping, wheels spinning,
smoke spuming in the sky.
On the ninth day they made us into
the image of animals, offspring of stray gases,
cosmic bastards in the gigantic unplanned
family of Man.
On the tenth day sick waters retched
and vomited their fish onto the sands.
Rivers expired, whales split
and the fate of seals was sealed.
On the eleventh day the moon lost her
virginity.
Her mystery is gone.
Inside her womb you will find a flag, equipment
and the footprints of Adam.
On the twelfth day the earth was burgled
and its riches went missing.
The Western World was observed
leaving the scene of the crime.
On the thirteenth day you could not see for miles
because the bad breath of civilisation
hung like gauze curtains in the sky.
On the morning of the fourteenth day
we rehearsed for the end of the world
on the open deserts and beneath the mountains.

By lunchtime our armies were massed on the
borders
waiting to go out and play,
waiting to add that finishing touch.

Steve Turner[2]

We have recognized the interconnectedness that exists within the natural world, and we have heard the questions that science and theology pose for each other. Nowhere do these find clearer expression than in the environmental debate. No study of creation can ignore the care of the planet.

In 1989 a great outcry was gathering momentum about the destruction of the rainforest. Viewed from the European side of the Atlantic it made good sense to call for a moratorium – the destruction of the rainforest was causing environmental destruction, not only in Brazil, but also to the ozone layer, which meant that we also would suffer through the effects of global warming. However, in Brazil it looked a little different – I remember the headline in one of the leading newspapers, which I read in Brasilia: 'Has anyone asked the British and other Europeans where their forests have gone?'

There is a self-centred paternalism, or worse, hypocrisy, when rich western nations want to prevent the poorer developing nations from doing what they have already done, in using natural resources to further economic development. The just answer would be for the rich nations of the world to share their resources with the poorer nations to enable them to develop without further destruction of the environment.

There are important questions to be addressed: conservation; pollution; ecology; stewardship; and justice, as we seek for a theology for earthkeeping.

The reality of the situation

The earth's surface and climate

The world climatic pattern produces extremes of climate, including the deserts of Africa and South America, and the monsoon cyclones of South East Asia. The margins of the earth's tectonic plates are the site of earthquakes and volcanic activity.

When a major earthquake occurs we could too easily blame God. The disastrous result for society is, at least in part, due to the moral evil of human irresponsibility. With the help of modern science we are able to

117

predict where and when disasters of this kind are likely to take place. So countries which are rich in resources and technology could counter such anticipated problems and avoid the worst effects if they had the will-power to accept the economic costs; for example, houses need not be built along an earthquake zone, and farmers need not farm on the side of Mount Etna. Poorer countries cannot themselves take evasive action; unless developed countries are willing to share their wealth, their living space and their expertise with others less advantaged, large populations will go on living – for example – on the coastal flood plains of Bangladesh. Thus, raising the moral question of the goodness of God also involves a moral issue for us. We can do something about the situation. We come face to face with God who, in his self-limiting love, gives freedom of choice to his creation, and who himself lives with the consequences of such an action. We have the God of love, revealed in his creation and in the Cross of Christ.

The world's population

Delicate checks and balances in the natural world have kept the population of most species at a constant level – the one exception is human beings: it is estimated that 300,000 years BP the human population of the world was about 1 million; 10,000 BP, 5 million; 2000 BP (AD 1), 250 million; AD 1800, 1,000 million; AD 1900, 2,000 million; AD 1980, 4,000 million; and by AD 2000 it is expected to stand at over 6,000 million. Better nutrition, control of disease through immunization, and improved sanitation have led to lower infant mortality and a resulting rise in population, which is a geometric progression. But in 1980 one fifth of the population were destitute. 'The bottom line,' says Sean McDonagh, 'is that in most Third World countries the population will be controlled. There is a limit to the carrying capacity of particular bioregions, and famine, starvation and death can take over.'[3] The question for the world is whether we will control population in a caring humane way or do nothing and watch the more violent control of population unfold before our eyes.

The atmosphere and biosphere

Atmosphere

The greenhouse effect is the earth heating up as a result of the burning of fossil fuels, building up CO_2 gas in the atmosphere. Ozone depletion is mainly caused by chlorofluoro-carbons (CFCs) used in fridges and air-conditioners, which react with ozone to produce chlorine monoxide. Sulphur dioxide, produced in large quantities by power stations and other industries in which coal and oil are burnt, combines with water in the atmosphere to become the main source of acid rain.

The impact of global warming will be seen in: i) Sea level changes, river flow, and groundwater levels. In low lying countries a rise of one metre in sea level by AD 2050 would be devastating; for example, over 6 million people in Bangladesh live below the 1m contour. ii) Deforestation will lead to both drought and flood. iii) Drier climates will have a great effect on agriculture. iv) There could be up to 3 million new environmental refugees each year – 150 million by the year 2050. v) The cost of these changes is estimated as 1% of Gross World Product, but twice as much for developing countries as for the industrialized nations. To this we must add the cost in human terms.[4]

Rainforests

As many as 80% of animal and plant species are found in the rainforests. They are being destroyed along with the forests. Forests are cleared to meet the First World's demand for tropical timber, or when agriculture is intensified to service foreign debt or to feed the growing population. But rainforests are the most important living system on earth, stabilizing the world's climate – 60% of the rainfall is held and transpired back to the atmosphere. The forests also lock up billions of tons of carbon. When forests are destroyed and the wood burned, carbon dioxide is released into the atmosphere, adding to the greenhouse effect. In addition to this, tribal cultures are being destroyed.

Ecosystems

Scientists are emphasizing the delicate balance of nature. Ecology is not a chain of cause and effect but a web of interconnectedness. 'Once we learn that the lives of snails and sparrows are linked to our own in a dozen ways, the meaning of ecology gradually expands to include every other aspect of human life and well-being.'[5]

Resource depletion

We consume the capital on which our economy is built, be it fossil fuels or ocean plankton; it is irreplaceable! The technological/silicon chip revolution is greedy for energy, and this in turn leads to increased pollution. In the 1970s the solution was seen as zero growth, but the revolution continues.

Economics

Third World debt is the result of high interest rates in First World countries, depressed commodity prices, protectionist policies, and a host of other unfair trading arrangements which make debt repayment impossible. This affects the local farmer who is vulnerable to any loss of harvest (forcing him to borrow and face high interest charges), and to increasing costs of fuel and fertilizer, while the price he receives for his crop is unchanged or even falls. The control of commodity prices is in the hands of the rich nations.[6]

A huge financial haemorrhage is taking place from poor to rich countries, with the result that the developing countries cannot feed their people.[7]

We should be aware that there can be a lethal spiral: Population growth → ecological crisis → social conflict. In poorer countries this is already happening. Shortages of water, forests, and especially fertile land, coupled with rapidly expanding populations causes great hardship.[8] People put pressure on land, which leads to destruction of the environment, resulting in famine, migration, ethnic and religious tension; and as society breaks down, the population continues to grow.

Changing views and emphases

Science

Modern cosmology has discovered a finely tuned universe, in which human beings appear to be woven into the fabric since its beginning. An expanding universe with a beginning and an end, exhibiting design and apparent purpose, suggests God the creator. Natural disasters, suffering, and man-made pollution are consistent with the universe being the creation of a self-limiting God, who gives choice to his creation. Here is our understanding of a God who accompanies and suffers with his creation. A universe which moves from Big Bang to Big Crunch or Heat Death, and in which there is a delicate balance between producing life and destroying it, forces us to consider carefully both our own future and our care of the planet. Here is our understanding of the place of humanity in creation, both as *imago Dei* and as stewards of creation.

Ecology has brought to light the unforeseen effects which human interference with natural processes often has; and this is why we can no longer plead inadvertence as the excuse for technological excess. Without a moral perspective, two attitudes can arise in science: i) Technological pragmatism, seen as an aspect of management. 'The ethical questions are not faced explicitly; the solution to a problem consists in finding an appropriate technique to control or eliminate it.'[9] This view is anthropocentric. ii) Evolutionary humanism, where the theory of evolution is the overriding ontological principle. Humans as the most complex product of the process are able to control and determine the development of the planet.

Philosophy

We have seen the emergence of ecological mysticism, with an appeal, by some, to eastern religions or to *Gaia* – a personification of nature. There is a desire for a closer, more wholesome, relationship with nature. Much of the so-called 'New Age' thinking embraces 'an astrological evaluation which sees the year 2000 as a passage from the age of "Pisces", equated with the Christian era, to the age of "Aquarius", an era of universal harmony and brotherhood between human beings and between humankind and nature.'[10]

The eco-crisis makes us rethink our view of the earth and our relationship to it. Ecology has its own fascination, for at least two reasons: it stresses the connectedness of all things, and it touches on the mystery of life itself. Here is fertile ground for worldview thinking.

There are three focuses within green religion:

1 *Creation spirituality.* Matthew Fox argues for the replacement of fall/ redemption theology by a creation-centred one, which he sees as 'an optimistic progression, as opposed to an acceptance of disorder and a need for redemption and reconciliation'.[11]

2 *Gaia* – earth as a living organism. Gaia was the Greek goddess who personified earth. Such ideas disappeared with Enlightenment rationalism, but have now re-surfaced with ecology. James Love-lock,[12] the leading advocate of Gaia, stresses the dynamic connection between the physical earth and its life-forms – the evolution of life-forms is closely coupled with the evolution of their physical and chemical environment. Earth is a planetary body that adjusts and regulates itself. Lovelock sees the world and its atmosphere is a self-

regulating negative feedback system. Human life is one element in an interacting but unitary organism. Gaia has become for some a divine entity, where green science becomes the justification for pantheism.

3 *Deep ecology* – biospheric egalitarianism, meaning that all things have an equal right to life. This is contrasted with shallow ecology, which merely deals with symptoms such as pollution.

Politics

The 1989 G7 Economic Summit set up a conference on Environmental Ethics, which advocated the practice of responsible stewardship. Perhaps a significant watershed was reached with the United Nations Conference on Environment and Development in Rio de Janeiro in 1992, which was attended by over 25,000 people. 160 countries signed the Framework Convention on climate change. The first principle of the 27 in the Rio Declaration reads: 'Human beings are at the centre of concerns for sustainable development. They are entitled to a healthy productive life in harmony with nature.' However, notes Houghton, 'despite such statements of principle from a body such as the United Nations, many of the attitudes which we commonly have to the Earth are neither balanced, harmonious nor sustainable.'[13] World governments continue to seek answers to global environmental issues.

Theology

Many have seen religion as the cause of failure, in the past providing the mandate for exploitation through the words of Genesis 1.28. Some have given voice to the view that Christians have had the flawed assumption that they were superior to nature and that nature's existence was to serve human beings. However, as Atkinson reminds us, we should also note that stewardship has been a major theme of Christian relationship to nature throughout the church's history. Amongst the Fathers of the Church, Justin Martyr, Theophilus of Antioch, and Tatian developed a theology of creation. Celtic spirituality was much more aware than we are of the presence of the divine in the world of nature. Amongst others we might note Francis of Assisi (1182–1226) and Hildegard of Bingen (1098–1178), who saw in the world the presence of God. Doctrinally, these people considered that God's image was to be seen in the trustworthiness and responsibility of human beings; and emphasized that the Hebrews saw kingship as servanthood.[14]

The fact that a biblical text was frequently misinterpreted should not be allowed to usurp its correct interpretation.

In recent years the church has begun to speak in the ecology debate. For example, Paragraph 5 of the Lausanne Covenant, *Christian Social Responsibility* (July 1974) begins:

> We affirm that God is both the Creator and the Judge of all men. We therefore should share his concern for justice and reconciliation throughout human society and for the liberation of men from every kind of oppression.

This statement was set against the background of the oil crisis of 1973, when OPEC raised world oil prices by 70%; the growing ecological awareness of the late 1960s; and the needs of the poor of the Third World, brought to the attention of the West through TV coverage of starvation in India, and more significantly the famine in Ethiopia.[15] There was a recognition that in living under the authority of Scripture, one could not be selective.

The Church of England has had a working party studying environmental issues since the mid-1970s. In 1991 its Board of Social Responsibility produced a statement that included the following:

> Stewardship implies caring management, not selfish exploitation; it involves a concern for both present and future as well as self, and a recognition that the world we manage has an interest in its own survival and well-being independent of its value to us.[16]

The World Council of Churches' consultation on 'Sharing Life' called for commitment to putting the marginalized at the centre of all decisions and actions as equal partners; to identifying with the poor and the oppressed, and their organized movements; and to mutual accountability and power.[17] More recently in the UK the Jubilee 2000 Charter (published by the Jubilee 2000 Coalition in 1996) has the fundamental aim of liberating the poorest nations from the burden of the backlog of unpayable debt owed by their governments, to international financial institutions or to commercial banks.

Biblical perspectives

God's involvement

God does not stand outside his creation; he is involved with it, sustaining it by his power.[18]

God continues with his work; in the imagery of Genesis, the seventh day of Genesis 2.1–3 has not brought creation to an end, but runs out into history. We see this also in the Old Testament picture of God accompanying his people through the wilderness as pillar of cloud or of fire; in the New Testament story of the incarnation; and in the church's experience of the presence and direction of the Holy Spirit.

Genesis 1.1—2.4a

The Priestly tradition (dated in the period from Exile to second Temple) proclaims God as the creator; all that he creates is good; there is no distinction between material and spiritual aspects of creation. For human beings to 'have dominion' over nature is a challenge to human beings to act with God, imitating his loving kindness and faithfulness with the whole of creation. The seventh day is the climax, the place where all of creation, including human beings, join in the worship of God.

Genesis 2.4—3.24

The Yahwist tradition, a few hundred years older than P, is a more earthly account – the master potter carefully moulding his creation.[19] God gives humans his Spirit and places them within the garden to till it and keep it.

The ordering of creation

From the Genesis account of creation we recognize that order is at the heart of God; it is his nature. We see the creator being free to exercise his will in all that he does, but God's acts are not fickle or arbitrary; his will is constrained by his character. Creation is an expression of God's creative purpose.

The Bible affirms order: God opens up the mystery of creative order to Job;[20] Yahweh offers reassurance through Deutero-Isaiah of his power to bring order;[21] and Paul points to God's nature revealed in his creation.[22]

God revealed

The Bible presents us with the revelation of God. In the Psalms we read of God's glory and handiwork revealed in the universe;[23] Jesus affirms that the signs of nature are dependable;[24] and Paul recognizes that God's nature is revealed in his creation.[25] Modern science is discovering a universe exhibiting design, in which human beings have a central place.

Land

To whom does the earth belong? 'The earth is the LORD's',[26] and God has given it to us.[27] But it is leasehold – to rule on God's behalf.[28] Our unique relation with God leads to our ability to think, choose, create, love, pray, and exercise control. Research, discovery, and invention in biology, chemistry, physics, and other spheres, and in all the triumphs of technology, are part of our God-given role. We co-operate with the processes of nature, we do not create them. God has entrusted us – we are caretakers, not landowners. The Year of Jubilee teaches us that we do not hold the freehold rights.[29] Goods are meant for everyone; they are to be shared.

Covenant

God commanded Noah to conserve nature,[30] and after the Flood God established his covenant with all of creation.[31] The new covenant after the Flood reminds us that we are always looking from the side of a broken creation. God's saving of creation is seen in God's heart, as he remembers Noah.[32] The land is still to be fertile. But then we are led into a discussion of what sort of relation creatures should have towards one another. How can the violence and the killing be in accordance with God's absolute sovereignty? The answer is that paradise is lost. The groaning of creation starts here.[33] God is in sovereign control. 'Respect for Yahweh's sovereignty, care for the earth, concern for the poor, sensitivity to the needs of both wild and farm animals, all come together in Ex. 23.10–12.'[34] In our modern world where economics rather then ecology controls our farming there may be good reason to listen to God's plan. The Old Testament concept of *shalom* implies more than an absence of war; it involves a healthy creative relationship with God and other humans, and it must now include the well-being of all creation.

Justice

Gustavo Gutierrez distinguishes three meanings of poverty: i) material poverty – the lack of economic goods which are necessary for life; ii) spiritual poverty; and iii) a biblical understanding that recognizes that poverty contradicts the meaning of the Mosaic religion and the Christian faith, which is to give people dignity.[35] There must be the elimination of the exploitation and poverty that prevents the poor from being fully human. Christians should have a solidarity with the poor and should oppose poverty. A key test is the Jubilee manifesto of Luke 4.18–19 – the words of the prophets had fallen on deaf ears and then the Messiah came. The Jubilee command calls for the restoration of the land to its original owners and peoples, which is so much an issue in Central and South America. Genesis and Deuteronomy present a picture of God's intent that land should not be merchandise. It is for the common good, not for private enterprise; it is the inheritance of all generations as God's free gift.

Sin and redemption

Sin describes the main feature of environmental destruction. Sin alienates people from God, from their fellow human beings and from the natural world.

In Jesus Christ there will be a new creation.[36] To believe in Christ in this world is to believe against reality – Christ is risen but we live in a world of suffering, pain, and destruction. Ours is hope; now we see salvation for all creation only appearing in outline. But this cannot be a cheap hope, we must act in hope; the Spirit gives us the possibility to be what we are to become, namely, the children of God.

A theology for earthkeeping

The value that God places on all life

It is important to avoid compartmentalizing ecological reflection, separating human concerns from those of the whole of nature. Not only do we understand that rainforests and their unique flora and fauna are being lost; we also recognize that tribal cultures are being destroyed. It is not only that finite resources are being consumed at an alarming pace, but also that people's lives are being exhausted, their needs and their dreams ignored.

As we noted earlier, Gustavo Gutierrez challenges the church to recover the biblical call to give all people the dignity which is achieved through the elimination of exploitation and poverty, which prevent the poor from being fully human. Jesus said, 'I have come that they may have life, and have it to the full.'[37]

Sharing and giving

We noted earlier that the Old Testament concept of *shalom* involves a creative relationship with God, with other human beings, and with the whole of creation. There must be a oneness: we who celebrate the new covenant in bread and wine must share with all, must love all.[38]

When we considered the occurrence of natural disasters (flood, cyclone, hurricane, earthquake, volcanic eruption), we noted our abilities to predict and counter their effects. Developed nations need to share not only their expertise, but also their technology, resources, and living space with poorer nations. Christians, who claim to live under the authority of Scripture, cannot be selective in their attention to its content.

Cancelling all debts

Third World debt is largely the result of the operation of the financial markets and trading policies of First World countries. Christians should challenge such policies and recognize the declaration of the Year of Jubilee that Jesus made at the beginning of his ministry.[39]

Stewardship

Stewardship implies caring management, not selfish exploitation; it involves a concern for both present and future as well as self; and a recognition that the world in which we live has an interest in its own survival and well-being independent of its value to human beings.

It may appear important to control the depletion of finite resources, such as fossil fuels and ocean plankton, for they are irreplaceable. But this raises questions for Christian concern to help developing nations who need to exploit these resources merely to survive. The destruction that humans bring to creation does question whether we are in control or able to be stewards. The way in which other species become resistant to pesticides, insecticides, and penicillin questions whether we *can* be stewards of the natural world. Our control may be only partial.

It has been noted that both Christian and secular agencies have latched onto the concept of stewardship in examining the way in which humans should relate to the rest of the natural world. However, Clare Palmer warns that 'the use of stewardship can represent an easy retreat to a comfortable concept which avoids coming to terms with deeper philosophical and theological issues inextricably interwoven with the environmental crisis.'[40] We can fall into the danger of thinking of God as the absentee landlord, who leaves human beings in charge. Stewardship may also be a barrier to understanding God as dwelling in his creation. We should listen to those environmentalists who, with no understanding of God, take the view that we do not inherit the earth from our ancestors, but borrow it from our children. We should also remember that it is God who calls us to be stewards. There are far-reaching consequences if we forget about stewardship – we run the risk of forgetting grace and gratitude, and of changing our basic outlook from stewardship to *ownership*. Stewardship is not only a matter of how wealth is distributed, but also how it is acquired. Wealth is acquired from the finite resources of the planet, so stewardship must be concerned with issues of ecological and political exploitation – respecting the integrity of creation. The biblical word 'dominion' must no longer be misunderstood as domination. 'As awareness of the consequences of consuming non-renewable resources or of permanently affecting the ecological balance increases, so does our accountability, both to God and to our neighbour, of this and of future generations.'[41]

The idea of the natural world as a resource belongs to a human-developed financial model – the idea that everything is there for the good of humanity. This leads us to consider justice. There is a danger that as long as we can justify something as benefiting humanity, it will be acceptable under a stewardship ethic. Destruction of woodland, wilderness, and wetlands for agriculture is justified to feed humans; and the flooding of river valleys, for hydro-electric power. Such views are entirely anthropocentric.

Justice

Development which pollutes and undermines life-support systems is a contradiction in terms. It is here that we will want to note the responsibility of richer nations in terms of justice. However, mere economic growth is not an indication of development; injustice prevails where people's basic needs are left unmet. We can take Attfield's example of the plight of the tribal people of the Arfak Mountains in Indonesia, who are being denied the opportunity to exploit their natural resources: 'it is morally unacceptable to claim . . . that the needs of future generations for intact rainforest there justify us in disregarding these current needs. For if future people's needs count, so do the needs of our contemporaries.'[42] Nor is it satisfactory to maintain that what fundamentally matters in morality is the integrity and stability of the biosphere, and to disregard the well-being of every individual. It can become an attempt to disown all the requirements of justice.

The uneven distribution, control, and use of natural resources are serious justice issues; and the rapid depletion of non-renewable natural resources raises the question of our responsibility to future generations. Poverty is a source of ecological destruction, but 'unless the poor have alternative sources of food and basic needs like fuel, they too will wantonly destroy whatever natural environment is around them.'[43]

Relationships

Sin results in broken relationships. The natural world is not the complete environment for human beings; God and his grace also form the human environment. We cannot reduce environment to a biological chain of vital processes. 'An adequate theology of the environment therefore involves God, the human person and nature; thus problems concerning the environment cannot be resolved in purely socio-political terms.'[44] There is often the danger of the ecology label being used by people to promote their own materialistic ideologies. It is totally unacceptable to follow the approach of certain ecologists who see the solution of the crisis of human beings and their environment in terms of population control. Such ideological manipulations have at their root an egoistic philosophy which in fact seeks to make life more pleasurable for wealthier countries by disregarding the interests of less well-developed nations.

We need a theology for earthkeeping which is holistic and not dualistic – separating out human beings as above the rest of the world; that has regard to God's immanence as well as his transcendence; and that is relational, recognizing the trinitarian God of creation.

A Christian response

Christians have a contribution to make. God created the earth, entrusted it to human beings, and will redeem the whole of creation.[45] We must learn to think and act ecologically; repent of extravagance, pollution, and wanton destruction; and recognize that human beings find it easier to subdue the earth than they do to subdue themselves. There is a need to be re-awakened to the gospel ethic, and recognize that human greed is at the root of the environmental crisis. There is a price to pay through fair prices for Third World goods and higher taxes to allow the support of development in Third World countries.

Christians face the task of articulating the gospel with relevance; of speaking up prophetically and relevantly about the environmental and social issues of our day; and of rediscovering a holistic doctrine of creation. Sadly, the church often misses the opportunity and others take on the task – this is particularly the case with the environment. The growth of the Green Movement is a clear example, where there has been little Christian involvement. The Jubilee 2000 Charter (published by the Jubilee 2000 Coalition in 1996), for example, has sought to present a Christian response to Third World debt, aiming, in response to Jesus' call to bring Good News to the poor, to free the poorest nations from their large financial debts. To achieve this liberation, and a return to sustainable development, they suggest the unrepeatable one-off remission of unpayable debts of the poorest countries by the year 2000.

> The native American Cree people have a saying: 'only when the last tree has been cut, the last river poisoned, and the last fish caught, only then you will realise that one cannot eat money.'[46]

9 A Doctrine of Creation

The heavens declare the glory of God;
the skies proclaim the work of his hands.'[1]

Credal belief

The Apostles' Creed reads as follows:

I believe in God the Father almighty,
maker of heaven and earth;
and in Jesus Christ, his only Son, our Lord,
who was conceived of the Holy Spirit,
born of the Virgin Mary,
suffered under Pontius Pilate,
was crucified, died and was buried.
He descended into hell.
The third day he rose again from the dead;
he ascended into heaven,
and sits at the right hand of God the Father almighty.
I believe in the Holy Spirit:
the holy, catholic Church,
the communion of saints,
the forgiveness of sins,
the resurrection of the body,
and the life everlasting.

Like all statements of belief, this creed is the result of theological
reflection upon people's experience of faith. It also would reflect their
experience of life in the world. Faith, if it is to stand the test of all life's
joys and woes, questions, and anxieties, must be able to make sense of
those experiences.

In our examination of the background to the Old Testament declara-
tions concerning creation and belief in the creator, we have discovered
that the people reflected upon their experiences and redefined their

faith. Through the defeat and despair of exile in Babylon, they reflected upon their own traditions, the religious mythologies of their captors, and upon their own experience of life and the world they inhabited. In the face of the religious beliefs of their conquerors, and in spite of the destruction of their homeland and religious centre of worship, they were able to declare that Yahweh, the covenant God of Israel and her history, was also the unique creator of the universe, and Lord of the nations. The creation struggle motif of Canaanite and Babylonian mythology is taken and used in portraying Yahweh's conquest of Israel's enemies, where the chaos god, Leviathan, is identified with Egypt and Babylon. In the creation story itself, Israel's God is the creator of all the monsters, they are not rival deities. The astral deities are denied their power; they too are Yahweh's creation, signs of his faithfulness, marking times and seasons. Human beings are important to Israel's God, they possess his character, they have a special relationship with God, and they are given the responsibility of caring for creation. From their place in Yahweh's creation, and their relationship with God, the creation narrative flows out into the people's history, where God accompanies them.

We see God portrayed as transcendent creator, yet immanent in the history of the people; he shares a covenant relationship, characterized by his grace, with the people; through this the trinitarian nature of God is expressed. All of creation is the place of God's activity and presence, but God's relationship is never coercive. God gives freedom to creation and as a result lives with the risk that such freedom poses. The story of God's people is one of self-centred rebellion, yet God's promise is the hope of redemption for the whole of creation. In the light of creation, covenant, freedom, and redemptive hope, people are called to worship. Worship is the climax of the creation story, of the covenant with Noah, and the response of the people to each experience of God in their history.

The New Testament reflection on creation and on the role of Christ in the creation of the universe was in the light of the birth, life, death, and resurrection of Jesus. The apostle John was able to take the Greek concept of *Logos*, and see Jesus as the Word, through whom God had created the universe and all of life.[2] In the letter to the church at Colossae, the apostle Paul recalls a hymn of the church that expresses the place of Christ in creation, and in the redemption of the church and the world.[3] Here we find the reflection that God is deeply and passionately involved in his world; he is no absentee landlord, but is indwelling and incarnate.[4] In Christ God will bring the whole of the universe back to himself, making peace (*shalom* – wholeness) through the Cross, both on earth and in heaven. This radical transformation has already begun through the presence of the Holy Spirit.[5]

We have a picture of a sacramental universe: all creation is in God; God is in all creation, celebrated in bread and wine.

Again we see that, in their theological reflection, in the light of their experience of Christ, the apostles declare that God is creator, transcendent and immanent, in covenant with people as the trinitarian God. The risk of freedom is seen in the Cross, but the hope of the redemption of creation is seen in the power of the resurrection and the transforming presence of the Holy Spirit. This is all celebrated in worship, through bread and wine,[6] as a foretaste of the worship of heaven and of a new creation.[7]

As we come to the end of our exploration of the understanding of creation, we will reflect upon all that makes up our experience: biblical witness; the traditions of the church of Christ; the current scientific understanding of the universe; and our own experience of God and the world.

God's transcendence and immanence

In the light of the views of modern cosmology and the life sciences, any doctrine of creation has to consider the concept of the beginning (and origin) of the universe, and the apparent unfolding of the Anthropic Principle, even though scientists express differing points of view.

The biblical witness is that God alone is eternal; he is the first and last. This excludes a dualistic view of matter and spirit, and also pantheism, whereby God might be seen as the force throughout the material world. The creator is Lord, who brings about creation through the Word. Genesis 1 shows the act of creation as the Word of the transcendent creative will. Even in the earlier account of God fashioning human beings, in Genesis 2, the power of the creator is clearly expressed. Eichrodt comments that throughout Genesis 1—11 the narrative 'points to the fact that a creature which in itself is totally impotent, with no inherent right to life, is called into moral fellowship with its Creator.'[8] We can see this as the gift of God, who can be pictured as a master craftsman fashioning his creation. The Hebrew word *yasar*, used in Genesis 2, is used elsewhere with the meaning to devise or conceive an idea or project. As Mason notes, the wonder and praise of God is not only for his wonderful designs, but for his bringing them to fruition. Israel's celebration moves from the creator of the universe to the creator of human beings and then to the Lord of history, who is working his purposes out.[9] This image provides us with a picture of God the craftsman whose purposes include beauty, order, and love, which he has the power to bring to expression, and which are seen in creation and especially in human beings.

We can suggest that creation is both dependent and chosen; it is dependent upon a creator, and is the intention of that creator. From the perspective of the New Testament we understand that God is love,[10] and is self-emptying in nature.[11] For such a God the creation of the universe becomes necessary as the place where these attributes can be expressed.

There is no conclusive proof that Israel did not think, in a similar way to other ancient Near Eastern peoples, that chaos existed first. However, there are passages that suggest that chaos is the creation of God (for example, Proverbs 8.22, where wisdom is the first created, and Psalm 148.3–5, where the waters above the heavens are called upon to praise Yahweh because he created (*bara*) them). Eichrodt believes that the picture in Genesis 1.2 of the primordial waters and darkness, through which the mighty wind rushes without rest or purpose, is a picture of complete non-existence, devoid of creative potential.[12] God is no first cause, but the creator who acts with absolute freedom. The universe comes into being through God's creative word. Moltmann maintains that the beginning is not in time: 'The beginning has no presuppositions at all.' There are no preconditions; it is *ex nihilo*. Created through God's free will, the world is created neither from pre-existent matter nor out of the divine being. Creation is not a demonstration of power but a communication of love.[13]

Science operates on the assumption of an ordered world, but we realize that the world's order is contingent – God could have made it otherwise. Following on from a Big Bang beginning, the deterministic laws of science are suggestive of design and order. We might suggest that the fine tuning of the initial conditions and ordered rationality of the created world derives from the transcendent rationality of the creator. Yet we look for a universe that is both intelligible and also relational. Intelligible is not the same as deterministic, for to be intelligible the universe must include purpose and choice. As in Mason's model of the craftsman, creativity includes choice, purpose, and intrinsic value. If we posit a universe governed by laws, we are left to ask why we have the laws. The answer to this question may be an existent being. But if, as cosmologists are now suggesting, there are many possible universes, we ask why this particular universe should exist. With an almost infinite number of possibilities, the answer might be to suggest that this universe is the choice of an existent being. We can propose that this universe is the choice of a creator, who chooses a contingent universe that expresses his nature (love, freedom, and relationship), and that is able to respond to the creator.

For Moltmann, an ecological doctrine of creation helps us in a new kind of thinking about God. The centre of this thinking is no longer the distinction between God and the world. The centre is the recognition of the presence of God in the world and the presence of the world in God.[14] The creator is present in creation as the Spirit. This relationship to creation is, for Moltmann, an intricate web of unilateral, reciprocal, and many-sided relationships:

> In this network of relationships, 'making', 'preserving', 'maintaining' and 'perfecting' are certainly the great *one-sided* relationships; but 'indwelling', 'sympathizing', 'participating', 'accompanying', 'enduring', 'delighting' and 'glorifying' are relationships of *mutuality* which describe a cosmic community of living between God the Spirit and all his created beings.[15]

God is both transcendent and immanent; this immanence is seen not only in the ecological relationships identified by Moltmann but also, as we have discussed in earlier chapters, in the model of an evolving universe, and in the evolutionary development of life on planet earth. However, it is the incarnation of God in Christ that supremely points to God's dynamic and intimate relationship with his world; this is the fullest expression of his immanence. We need to hold on to this self-revelation of God, for otherwise we may be left with a deism that emphasizes God's transcendent power, purpose, and mind, but which, in so doing, places him outside of the world and outside of our lives. Such a God is ineffectual once he has set creation in progress. Creation is seen by Christians as an act of free love. But the question we must try to answer is *how* God continues to act in love.

We cannot think of God's transcendence without his immanence. Evolution urges us to consider continuous creation, in which God is present to endure breaches of communication between systems, and to find new ways through his suffering to open up communication again when it has broken down. As Moltmann puts it, 'It is not through miraculous interventions that God guides creation to its goal and drives forward evolution; it is through passion, and the opening of new possibilities out of his suffering.'[16] The prophetic theology of God's creative acts in history[17] pushes us to understand this immanent activity as anticipating new acts of creation and the consummation of time. We can conclude that God is guiding an evolutionary process that includes not only law but chance and the emergence of novelty.

There is one final aspect under which we should understand the immanence of God, and it is a trinitarian one. John Macquarrie notes that Christian theology has used two models of creation: 'making' and 'emanation'.[18] While 'making' points to the transcendence of God, emanation – like that of the sun's rays from the sun – suggests something of the immanence and closeness of the relationship between God and the world. Making refers to a transcendent letting-be, and emanation has God putting himself into creation. The Christian faith finds the balance between these two most fully expressed in the incarnation of God in Christ. As the 'expressive Being' of God, the eternal Son is the agent through whom creation is brought into being;[19] he is generated or 'emanates' from the Father (as 'primordial Being'), and while creation itself is certainly not generated from God, the 'expressive Being' of God really enters into creation. Thus already in creation the transcendent God is intimately involved with his creation, and this is the basis for creator and creature becoming truly one in the incarnation. The Spirit is then to be seen as 'unitive Being', uniting God with himself in his triune being, and lifting the whole creation toward God in reconciliation.[20] The risk of creation is overcome and the potentiality is fulfilled as creatures participate in the life of God.[21]

A holistic creation

Therefore, the unity and coherence of the world is not found in a cosmological principle but in the personal will of Yahweh, the creator. We have to move away from the rational, reductionist approach that is dominated by objects and facts. Science now concurs that we have a better understanding if objects are seen in their relationships and environments, including the human observer. Life means to exist in relationship, communion and environments. Our motive for knowledge ceases to be in order to dominate, but rather becomes perception in order to participate. As Moltmann suggests, we can speak of this as a covenant with nature, or a psychosomatic totality, or a community of creation.[22]

This recognition of unity in God is seen in Genesis 2, but more clearly worked out in Genesis 1. This faith developed through the political upheavals of the eighth and seventh centuries BC. The view of the universe as a unified entity is given its fullest expression in the poetry of Psalm 104, of which Eichrodt says, 'here Israelite feeling for the natural order found the expression best suited to the absolute claims of belief in Yahweh'.[23] Creation is understood as part of history:

> a history determined on the one hand by the self-willed flight of the creature from that life-relationship with God which is essential to him, and on the other by God's activity, shaping history in an inexhaustible variety of ways in order to bring back to God those who are lost in alienation from him.[24]

God is the source and not the cause of creation.

Humankind depends on everything else; we see a mutual symbiotic union. Through the experience of the covenant, which is with God and creation, a sense of the oneness of the universe is apprehended. The unity is in a common, graduated sharing in God. Trigo suggests that the image of 'struggle' in the evolution of life is a projection of human society, and that faith in the oneness of creation will not allow us to see a polarized world.[25] Ecology hints to us that meaning is found in relationships – the significance of one thing is found in its connection to other things. We begin to presume meaning and significance even when we have not yet found it. There may be some chemical in a plant that will have great medical importance. Nothing is insignificant because everything is linked. Snyder observes that 'something about the ecology of our own lives and minds tells us these intricate patterns of inter-relationship constitute some deep meaning.'[26]

Ecology presents a picture of wholeness and distinction, with meaning arising from the relationship between the parts. Snyder contends that

> in the Christian tradition, philosophers and theologians have dealt with this issue of meaning and relationship in part through the doctrine of the Trinity ... God is Three-in-one ... The unity – perhaps the meaning – of God is found in the indivisible, ever-intercommunicating relationship of one-in-two, two-in-three, three-in-one. In the Christian view, meaning is therefore trinitarian and relational.[27]

> Believing that the patterns and linkages of the universe disclose, or at least signal, fundamental meaning is more plausible and more consistent with the nature of human mind and experience, however, even this is not convincing to everyone.[28]

Connectedness does not prove meaning. Only within our own lives is this meaning understood – it is my life that tells me what is the significance of ecology. Yet full meaning comes from the perception of a transcendent reality; it comes through faith in a personal God.

It may be helpful to consider the whole of the universe as sacramental, as a place where God encounters us with his grace. In the view of the Reformers, a sacrament depends entirely on a word of promise given by God. The Genesis accounts of creation certainly fulfil this criterion. The bread, wine, and water of the sacraments lend themselves as instruments of God's grace because God made them, and they are part of creation. Baillie believes that when Christianity took these as sacraments it was because this universe is a sacramental kind of place. However, he contends that there needs to be a relation with the historic divine revelation to make a real sacrament, and that therefore 'the sacrament speaks only to faith'.[29] We can, with Baillie, make reference to Calvin's view of the rainbow in Genesis 9. Calvin writes:

> If any dabbler in philosophy, in order to deride the simplicity of our faith, contends that such a variety of colours is the natural result of the refraction of the solar rays on an opposite cloud, we must immediately acknowledge it; but at the same time we will deride *his* stupidity in not acknowledging God as Lord and Governor of Nature, who uses all the elements according to His will for the promotion of His own glory. And if He had impressed similar characters on the sun, on the stars, on the earth, and on the stones, they would all have been sacraments to us . . . Shall not God be able to mark His creatures with His Word, that they may become sacraments, though before they were mere elements.[30]

Nature can, in this way, express God's mercy and faithfulness. Jesus presents us with just such a picture, when he speaks of the 'lilies of the field'.[31] Jesus saw God's creative love and care in the flowers of the field, and to his faith, like the rainbow, these flowers are sacramental. Baillie concludes that

> It is only when God speaks and awakens human faith that the natural object becomes sacramental. But this can happen to material things only because this is a sacramental universe, because God created all things visible and invisible.[32]

The Incarnation speaks of God's deepest possible involvement with creation; the Resurrection is the hope of a destiny for all creation; the Ascension is the possibility of being caught up in eternity with God; and

Pentecost marks out God's continuing involvement with his world now, with the possibility of new creation. The Spirit works through the whole of creation – it is the whole of creation that groans.

God's covenant and grace

We have seen that God is both transcendent to and immanent in creation, but we also need to discuss how God relates to creation. In questioning the relationship of God with creation, Page observes that the interventionist God is a powerful onlooker; the God of liberation theology is a suffering onlooker, while process theology holds out nothing more than the God who shares the experiences of creation.[33] If love is the fundamental character of God,[34] it is relevant to ask how love acts. In freedom and love we might expect God to form and maintain relationships with all creatures as they live and develop. This is expressed both in God's letting-be, and in his accompanying of creation. Page is right to state that from such a presence all kinds of possibilities arise: particularly possibilities of relationship in creaturely freedom and love.[35]

Van Wolde, as we noted in Chapter 3, drew attention to the use in Genesis 6—9 of *yhwh* and *elohim*. *Elohim* is used of God standing by himself, independent of the created world bringing destruction to the whole created order; *Yhwh* is used of the God of human beings, who is in contact with the creatures and gives them meaning. It is *Yhwh* who regrets and feels pain, as he looks on creation and human beings whom he is about to destroy.[36] The use of 'the Lord God' in Genesis 2 also combines *yhwh* and *elohim*: he is the sovereign creator of the universe (*elohim*) and the intimate covenant God of relationship with humans (*yhwh*). The sovereign God shapes the man out of the dust and breathes his Spirit into him, but there is also God's loving concern for all of the man's needs, including companionship. God's action is understood as establishing and maintaining relationship, but, as we know, human relationships are often fraught with failure and difficulty.

The exemplar of the true nature of the relationship with God is Jesus. Jesus is free to act and speak, he takes risks, and he feels the pain of rejection. He does not present divine power removed from the experience of human life; the Kingdom is amongst them. The Cross shows the cost of maintaining relationship in the face of opposition. We can agree with Page that:

> From that perspective the resurrection is not the happy ending to a sad story, but the demonstration that God was there through it all and that

the darkness of the cross has not put out the light of love. To see this and be changed by it is to find salvation. The concurrence of Jesus with God is for Christians *the* demonstration of 'what God does'.[37]

Creation and salvation are not separate; God has always been there in freedom and love. In Jesus the possibility and presence of God with us become visible and effective; and Jesus invites others to share in this relationship – the Kingdom of God. From a Christian perspective we see creation together with its future, in which it will be perfected, as the Kingdom of glory. This takes place here on earth through God's Spirit, where human beings are in true relationship with God, who himself indwells his creation. It is here that a community of creation comes into being.

In the Old Testament, Yahweh is not part of the world process. The powerful God of the covenant is the single will behind creation. As covenant God, the creator is seen from the start to have the characteristics of personal and spiritual activity, together with moral purpose. The sabbath of creation shows that the world was orientated toward redemption from the beginning. Moltmann helpfully observes that 'when people celebrate the sabbath they perceive the world as God's creation, for in the sabbath quiet it is God's creation that they are permitting the world to be.'[38] For Israel the sabbath principle is extended through the sabbath year, when human relationships with creation are further defined – the land is given rest;[39] and then through the Year of Jubilee, when slaves are freed, debts cancelled, and the land returned to its original tribal designations.[40] For the Christian church, it is through Christ's death and resurrection that the first day of the week is celebrated as the first day of the new creation.

We draw on the whole of Scripture, Old and New Testaments, in recognizing that God reveals himself as the creator, preserver, and saviour of the world and all life. The experience of exodus, covenant, and promised land led to an understanding of the world as God's good creation. The experience of the ministry, death, and resurrection of Christ has led to an understanding of God's desire to redeem a broken creation. The Scriptures embrace the beginning and the end: Genesis 1.1 to Isaiah 65.17; and John 1.1 to Revelation 21—22; both creation and salvation.

The Bible is fairly clear that God wills human freedom to exist, in order to allow the existence of human responsibility for choosing righteousness or sin. God is the one and only creator, who calls Abraham and his descendants into a special relationship of loyalty and love. God teaches his people through his prophets, and looks for all humans to acknowledge his power and glory. Creaturely actions may frustrate the intentions of the creator, but, says Ward, the final purpose of the creator is not frustratable.[41] God allows the freedom to choose justice or self-will; he punishes injustice and promises fulfilment of relationship with God for all who turn to him.

As we noted earlier, Fiddes is right to draw our attention to the nature of God's project in making persons. He suggests that when we are dealing with persons, we cannot separate the road from the destination.[42] He proposes then that the risk upon which God has embarked is real and serious, though not a total one. God has a certain hope in the *fact* of the end, which shifts creation onto an altogether new level of existence; but there is a genuine openness about the route and therefore the *content* of the end, which is the nature of the persons who are being reconciled. So there is room for tragedy as well as for triumph in God's victory over suffering. In the final vision of God, the worshippers will not be disappointed, but God knows that they may not have reached their full potential.

At the heart of this view of the world is the immanent suffering of God, feeling pain in his relationship with his creation which is in the mixed condition of progress and decline. That God suffers is undeniable, and that God is fulfilled (in some way) through creation must also be true, but this does not imply that God is changed in his inner being by creation. We might consider the analogy that Fiddes employs, of that between God and a creative artist who sets out with the desire to paint a picture.[43] The artist has the possibility of the finished work in his mind, but the actual painting has new elements within it, which come about as he plays with the materials at his disposal – the variety of brushes, textures, and paints. So God uses the materials of free personalities, from whom he looks for a response in achieving his purposes. This analogy shows that while the picture may change, the divine artist himself remains essentially unchanged, with the exception of the pain that comes with disappointment in those who fail to respond to his love.

We recognize that God's relationship with creation is expressed in his covenant love, which includes creaturely freedom and divine risk-taking, creaturely rebellion and divine redemption.

A redeemed creation

As we stated in Chapter 6, the Incarnation speaks of God's deepest possible involvement with creation; the Resurrection is the hope of a destiny for all creation; the Ascension is the possibility of being caught up in eternity with God; and Pentecost marks out God's continuing involvement with his world now, with the possibility of new creation. The Spirit works through the whole of creation. The christological centre of the Christian faith was foreshadowed in our discussion of creation, where the transcendent-immanent relation between God and all life is already to be found. The Spirit is seen moving over the waters of chaos, and Paul can speak of creation groaning as it awaits the fruit of the Spirit in human beings.[44]

So we see that Christians have a contribution to make. God created the earth, entrusted it to human beings, and will redeem the whole of creation.[45] Part of redemption lies in human repentance of extravagance, pollution, and wanton destruction of the environment. There needs to be a response to Jesus' call to bring Good News to the poor, which means action, maybe beginning with the Jubilee 2000 campaign call to liberate the poorest nations from the burden of the backlog of unpayable debt owed by their governments to international financial institutions.

The understanding of human responsibility as stewardship still has a place, as we discussed in Chapter 8. The harmonious relationship between humans and nature was given a prominent place by the UN Conference on Environment and Development in Rio de Janeiro in 1992, but despite statements of principle from a body such as the United Nations, many of the attitudes toward the earth do not address the problems fully. We have responsibility for all living things – there are interdependences of all living systems. Lovelock,[46] for example, argues that the ecosystems of the earth are closely tied to their physical and chemical environments, so that it can be suggested that the ecosystems and their environment can be considered as one organism with an integrated 'physiology'. We have also seen that modern cosmology through the discovery of fine tuning and the anthropic principle is presenting a picture of human beings having a central place in the development of the universe. Yet we should maintain that some consideration be given to the interests and non-derivative value of all creatures, who although incapable of preferences, have a worth of their own, for example in the form of capacities for growth, reproduction, healing, and health.

There is a need to address global injustice, and in this the role of consumers can have far-reaching effects. Robin Attfield notes that

> in the limited area over which individuals have some measure of control, decisions affecting the life or death of distant people, of future generations and of entire living species are liable to be made; and once again the values elicited by environmental ethics and environmentally sensitive decision-making will continue to be potentially vital.[47]

The future is in our hands; as John Houghton concludes: 'We are not short of statements of ideals. What tend to be lacking are the capability and resolve to carry them out.'[48] Stewardship is difficult, but we are not on our own, we act in partnership with God, through the presence of the Holy Spirit.

God's trinitarian nature

The Trinity expresses the being of God in the Godhead. If God's essence is love, then he is seen in self-giving, in calling other beings into being, with whom love is shared.

The Son of Man is the fulfilment of humanity in God, and as such Jesus is the foreshadowing of that hope for all creation. Ward states that 'the Spirit makes present and applies the redemptive power of God which took form in Jesus, and thus the idea of the Trinity takes shape.'[49] While the Old Testament saw God as an interactive, morally purposive Will, the New Testament goes further, as Ward explains:

> God enters into the historical process to include humanity, and thereby ultimately all creation, in the divine being. The controlling model is not so much of an external Will as of an inward and unitive Love, an infinite Divine Life in which all created things can share.[50]

The concept of God as Trinity emerges through the idea that God, as the creator and Father of the universe, and the source of its being, is also the Father of Jesus Christ, and of the Spirit, who enters into created, alienated being to reconcile it to the divine life. Macquarrie sees that both transcendence and immanence are expressed in the Son, as Expressive Being: 'for Expressive Being, the outgoing life of God, is not only agent in creation but does really enter into creation.'[51] God is both transcendent in creative power and immanent in reconciling love, and as Holy Spirit reconciles creation to the Father, transforming created being into participation in the divine. Ward states that in Jesus 'this transformation is effected fully in a human life, and the at-one-ment of alienated creation and perfect Creator is realised.'[52]

We recognize that Christ is the ground for the existence and salvation of all of creation.[53] Basing our thinking on the Wisdom literature,[54] we recognize that God's eternal Wisdom and Word have been revealed in Christ, through whom the world is created and in whom it is sustained. Moltmann maintains that the outpouring of the Spirit for Christians belongs to the eschatological experience of salvation, and is the guarantee.[55] The experience of the Spirit is of God dwelling in his creation to preserve and reconcile it. The Spirit is creative not created, breathed forth by the creator. Through the Spirit, God is present with his creation, suffering and sighing.[56]

The Christian doctrine of creation builds on the revelation of Christ and the experience of the Spirit; the One who sends the Son and the Spirit is the creator, revealed as Father. The understanding of creation as the activity of the triune God holds together God's transcendence and immanence. If we emphasize transcendence, we arrive at the deism of Newton and some modern cosmologists, whereas if we emphasize immanence, we are in danger of pantheism. Moltmann is right to note that the conception of creating the world is not the same as causing it; we move away from the view of God as First Cause. If the creator is himself present in his creation by virtue of the Spirit, then his relationship is an intricate web of unilateral, reciprocal and many-sided relationships, as we noted earlier.

The trinitarian doctrine of creation preserves this tension between God who creates the world, and who enters into it; who calls it into existence, and who manifests himself in it. God in the world and the world in God.[57] Human beings correspond to the relationship of God to themselves; to the whole of creation; and to the inner relationships of God to himself – the eternal, inner love of God.[58] This is fully revealed in Christ.

A worshipping creation

In worship, Israel celebrated in song their deepest faith in God as their creator, sustainer and redeemer. He was the God of the covenant, related to Israel as his people and to the world as his creation. Israel gave praise to God who was active in the world and who, through his mighty deeds, had redeemed them from slavery and who continued to walk with them in good times and bad. In the Psalms, the theme of praising God as creator is almost as common as praising God as saviour.[59] In Psalm 148 the whole of creation is called to praise God; and in Psalms 65 and 104 the faithfulness of God in creation is expressed in worship. Creation itself gives testimony to the goodness and power of its creator,[60] as does the unique place given to human beings.[61]

The Fathers of the Church, such as Justin Martyr, Theophilus of Antioch, and Tatian, developed a theology of creation, often elaborated in opposition to the prevailing gnostic dualism. They affirmed the goodness of creation, created by God *ex nihilo*, but did not separate natural theology from Christology. McDonagh notes the sensitivity of the Greek Church to the created world in a prayer attributed to St Basil the Great (c.330–79):

> O God, enlarge within us the sense of fellowship with all living things, our brothers, the animals, to whom thou gavest the earth as their home in common with us.

> We remember with shame that in the past we have exercised the high dominion of man with ruthless cruelty, so that the voice of the earth, which should have gone up to thee in song, has been a groan of travail.

> May we realise that they live not for us alone but for themselves and for thee and that they love the sweetness of life.[62]

Celtic spirituality was much more aware of the presence of the divine in the world of nature. It is clear that Celtic spirituality drew upon the pre-Christian traditions associated with the sun, with harvest, springs, rivers, and holy wells; and Celtic saints are often associated with animals. Such experience of God, and his closeness and involvement in the ordinary everyday life of people was and remains a feature of Celtic religion, and of the revived Celtic Christianity.

Abbess Hildegard of Bingen (1098–1178), poet, musician, painter, visionary, botanist, and herbalist, wrote poetry reminiscent of the pre-Christian Celtic religion. She celebrated the feminine, fertility dimension of creation, and saw a sensuous dimension to the love of the creator for creation. For her, nature evokes joy, wonder, praise, awe, and especially love.[63]

In similar manner, St Francis of Assisi (1182–1226) did not see the natural world from a utilitarian perspective, as providing food, clothing, and shelter for human beings. His writings reflect a sense of joy, wonder, praise, and gratitude for the gift of all life. He saw God's presence reflected in all creatures.

Modern scientists speak of a rational beauty in the universe; the universe appears to be marvellously, rationally transparent. The patterns of the physical world are intriguing; there is an order that is both beautiful and exciting, and scientists are often heard to use words like 'wonder' and 'awe' when considering their researches and results. Mathematical equations that explain aspects of cosmology are described as 'beautiful'. One of the greatest surprises that these patterns and results are showing is that the present state of the universe depends on a 'fine tuning' of the initial conditions that brought it into existence. Such reactions do not necessarily lead to faith, as may be seen in the views of Albert Einstein. God, for Einstein, was manifested in the laws of nature: impersonal, sublime, beautiful, indifferent to human beings, but still important to them. Einstein affirmed the religious sense of wonder and mystery when looking at creation, but could not accept the idea of a personal God. God was the great unknown and unknowable. Human beings were part of the mystery; he said, 'The most incomprehensible thing about the universe is that it is comprehensible.'[64]

Returning to the Genesis account of creation, we note its conclusion in the seventh day.[65] This is the climatic close of God's creative work. From the seventh day creation opens out into the ongoing story of God with his people and his world.

The sabbath is God's rest, which has been offered to us, to share in God's fellowship. While the Israelites in the wilderness missed out on the promised land,[66] the invitation to enjoy God's rest remains.[67] Human alternation between work and rest echoes God's alternation between work and rest in his creative activity. As Atkinson notes, God's rest is his delight in creation, looking with joy on his world and saying, This is good![68]

So, we are invited to share the rhythm of creation: engagement with life and work, and the opportunity to reflect on life in worship. Worship is not only a church activity, it is our offering of our life back to God, for him to enjoy; it is our enjoyment of his world. The climax of the creation is found in worship. It is in worship that we express our thanksgiving and our hope – thanksgiving for God's faithfulness and selfless love in creation; and we hope that all of creation will be restored and made new in Christ.

Postscript[1]

I am the Alpha and the Omega, the First and the Last,
the Beginning and the End.[2]

God in his trinitarian nature is both transcendent and immanent, sharing his covenantal relationship of grace with all creation. Creation is holistic, fallen, but has the hope of redemption; and is drawn into the worship of the Creator.

Once there was a Big Bang fireball, happening in finely-tuned conditions, resulting in the evolution of a universe that includes human life –
– *in the beginning God, who created this world full of possibilities.*

There is now a universe that displays design, that is suggestive of purpose; and an anthropic principle that envisages the evolution of human life at the heart of that purpose –
– *in the beginning God, who is the purposeful mind that is woven into the fabric of the universe.*

There is a rational universe, which is understood as rational by the rational minds of human observers –
– *in the beginning God, who is source of all rationality.*

There is a planet called Earth, where life has begun and developed, in simplicity and complexity, with natural selection and novelty, and with interconnected dependence –
– *in the beginning God, who has accompanied his creation, guiding its evolution at every faltering step.*

There is a world in which freedom of choice is accompanied by suffering and death –
– *in the beginning God, who in love has given freedom to his creation, and who in love will bring it to its final consummation in himself.*

There is a biosphere that has been, and is being exploited, polluted, and destroyed by human activity –
– in the beginning God, who saw that creation was good and who gave human beings responsibility for its care, and who will, at the end, redeem his creation.

There are Scriptures that speak of the creation of order out of chaos, light in the midst of darkness, the power and majesty of the physical universe, the variety and richness of the living world, and human beings in the image of God, created for relationship with their Creator –
– in the beginning God, who has revealed himself in creation, in the record of Scripture, and specifically in Jesus Christ.

In creation and in our own lives we recognize the power, the presence, the love, and the grace of the Creator, in whom we can trust, in whom lies our hope, and to whom we give our worship –
– in the beginning, and at our end, God.

CREATION IS NOT ENOUGH[3]

Almighty God, Creator;
the morning is Yours, rising into fullness.
The summer is Yours, dipping into autumn.
Eternity is Yours, dipping into time.
The vibrant grasses, the scent of flowers, the lichen on the rocks,
　the tang of seaweed,
All are Yours.
Gladly we live in this garden of Your creating.

But creation is not enough.
Always in the beauty, the foreshadowing of decay.
The lambs frolicking careless; soon to be led off to slaughter.
Nature red and scarred as well as lush and green.
In the garden also; always the thorn.
Creation is not enough.

Almighty God, Redeemer:
the sap of life in our bones and being is Yours:
lifting us to ecstasy.
But always in the beauty: the tang of sin in our consciences.

The dry lichen of sins long dead, but seared upon our minds.
In the garden that is each of us, always the thorn.

Yet all are Yours as we yield them again to You.
Not only our lives that You have given are Yours:
But also our sins that You have taken.
Even our livid rebellions and putrid sins:
You have taken them all away
and nailed them to the Cross!
Our redemption is enough: and we are free.

Notes

Introduction

1 D. Wilkinson, *God, the Big Bang and Stephen Hawking*. Monarch, Tunbridge Wells, 1993.

1 The Jews in Babylon Tell the Story of Creation

1 Psalm 137.1.

2 Lamentations 5.1–18.

3 John Bright, *A History of Israel*. SCM Press, London, 1972, p. 344.

4 Jeremiah 52.28–30.

5 Bright, *History of Israel*, p. 345.

6 Jeremiah 29.5–7.

7 These are the dates given by Walther Eichrodt, *Ezekiel*. SCM Press, London, 1970, p. 1.

8 Ezekiel 3.15; 8.1; 14.1; 33.30–3.

9 Ezekiel 37.1–3.

10 Rex Mason, *Propaganda and Subversion in the Old Testament*. SPCK, London, 1997, p. 52.

11 Walter Brueggemann, *Hopeful Imagination: Prophetic Voices in Exile*. SCM Press, London, 1992, p. 4.

12 Isaiah 43.18–19.

13 Jeremiah 32.6–15; Ezekiel 37.

14 Ezekiel 20.26, 42, 44; 34.30; 37.13, 14 etc.

15 Ezekiel 37.9–10; cf. Genesis 1.2; 2.7; 8.1.

16 Isaiah 40.6–8; 55.10–11.

17 Isaiah 55.12–13.

18 Isaiah 41.22–4.

19 Mason, p. 52.

20 Isaiah 56.1–8; 58.13–14.

21 Genesis 2.2–3; Bright, p. 349.

22 Gordon J. Wenham, *Genesis 1—15*. Word Books, Waco, 1987, p. 8.

23 Claus Westermann, *Genesis 1—11*. SPCK, London, 1984, p. 81.

24 Wenham, p. 9.

25 Others have noted that the Hebrew of Genesis 1.1–2 is ambiguous and could be interpreted as meaning that God acted by shaping and ordering a pre-existent chaos. Yet this would not undermine Wenham's and my own view that Genesis 1 bears

witness to the sole, supreme power of the one God, and is thus a rejection of much ancient mythology.

26 Genesis 1.21.

27 Genesis 1.6–10.

28 Mason, pp. 54–5.

29 Isaiah 44.28—45.4.

30 Isaiah 43.14–21.

31 Isaiah 40.28.

32 Isaiah 45.11–13, 18; 48.12–16.

33 Isaiah 40.27–31; 51.1–16.

34 Isaiah 41.16; 51.11; 52.9; 54.1; 55.1.

35 Isaiah 42.11–12.

36 Isaiah 42.10.

37 Isaiah 43.20.

38 Isaiah 44.23; 49.13; 55.12.

39 Isaiah 40.21–8; 44.24–8.

40 Isaiah 43.19.

41 Isaiah 54.9; see also 43.2.

42 Isaiah 55.3b–5.

43 Isaiah 43.14–21.

44 Isaiah 41.1–5, 21–29; 43.8–15; 44.6–20; 45.20–5.

45 Isaiah 46.1–2.

46 R.E. Clements, *Old Testament Theology: A Fresh Approach.* Marshall, Morgan & Scott, London, 1978, p. 75.

47 Daniel 3.59–90, Septuagint reading; see also Psalm 148. When faced with the choice of worshipping the gold image or death by burning, Shadrach, Meshach and Abednego say to Nebuchadnezzar: 'If we are thrown into the blazing furnace, the God we serve is able to save us from it, and he will rescue us from your hand, O king. But even if he does not, we want you to know, O king, that we will not serve your gods or worship the image of gold you have set up' (Daniel 3.17–18). Their psalm of praise, sung within the furnace, proclaims that every part of creation praises Yahweh. This song follows the pattern of the creation Psalm 148, which we will discuss in Chapter 3.

48 J.D. Barrow, *Theories of Everything.* Oxford University Press, Oxford, 1990, p. 9.

49 Ellen van Wolde, *Stories of the Beginning: Genesis 1—11 and Other Creation Stories.* SCM Press, London, 1996, p. 1.

50 Van Wolde, p. 177.

51 Van Wolde, p. 178.

52 Stanley L. Jaki, *Genesis 1 Through the Ages.* Thomas More Press, London, 1992, p. 28.

53 G. von Rad, *Genesis*. SCM Press, London, 1961.

54 Westermann, *Genesis 1—11*.

55 B.S. Childs, *Introduction to the Old Testament*. SCM Press, London, 1979, pp. 154–5.

56 G. von Rad, *Old Testament Theology, Volume One*. SCM Press, London, 1975, p. 140.

57 Mark 1.1.

58 John 1.1–5.

59 Wenham, *Genesis 1—15*, p. 10.

60 Jaki, *Genesis 1 Through the Ages*, p. 301.

61 Ephesians 1.9–10.

62 Walter Brueggemann, *Genesis*. John Knox Press, Atlanta, 1982, pp. 18–19.

2 The Creation Stories Told by the Babylonians and Others

1 Isaiah 40.18–19.

2 Psalms 19, 47, 65, 67, 93, 99, 104, 121, 148.

3 Isaiah 40, 45, 49, 60 and 65.

4 John 1.1–18; Colossians 1.15–20.

5 See W.E. Soothill, *The Three Religions of China*. Oxford University Press, London, pp. 154–5.

6 Cesare Emiliani, *Planet Earth: Cosmology, Geology, and the Evolution of Life and Environment*. Cambridge University Press, Cambridge, 1992, 1995, p. 2.

7 Emiliani, *Planet Earth*, p. 3.

8 Pedro Trigo, *Creation and History*. Burns & Oates, Tunbridge Wells, 1992, p. 90.

9 John Bright, *A History of Israel*. SCM Press, London, 1972, p. 39.

10 John Drane, *Introducing the Old Testament*. Lynx, Oxford, 1987, p. 48.

11 Artur Weiser (*The Psalms*, SCM Press, London, 1962, p. 666) says that this is one of the most beautiful poems in the psalter. 'The relation of this nature-hymn to the story of creation in the first chapters of Genesis is like that of a coloured picture to the clear lines of a woodcut.' The picture presented bears the influence of the poet's time; he makes use of the contemporary worldview; there are parallels with Babylonian, Egyptian, Greek, and Nordic mythology. Affinity with the hymn to the Sun composed by Egyptian king Akhenaten (fourteenth century BC) is evident. Leslie Allen (*Psalms 101—150*, Word Books, Waco, 1983, p. 28) noted parallels with Genesis 1 and the Egyptian hymn of Akhenaten. He says that there are marked similarities with the hymn to Aten, but the links with Genesis 1 show a clear Hebrew cosmology. A detailed comparison between Psalm 104 and Genesis 1 is given by John Day (*Psalms*, JSOT, Sheffield, 1990, pp. 41–2), who also notes the parallels with Akhenaten's hymn. He sees the strongest parallels with this fourteenth century BC 'heretical monotheistic worship' in verses 20–30 (excluding verse 26).

12 Life in Ur was culturally rich and comfortable. It was a place of polytheism and

Terah, Abram's father, traded in idols of the 300 plus deities. Terah and his family head out against the stream of Amorite migration, which was toward, rather than away from, Mesopotamia. The trade route from Ur to Haran was used by many merchants and traders and in Haran the religious life was similar to that of Ur. Terah and his family would have been comfortable there, but Abram is called to go on.

13 Psalms 74.14; 89.10. See also Isaiah 51.9; Job 26.13; Isaiah 27.1. Also John Day, *God's Conflict with the Dragon and the Sea: Echoes of a Canaanite myth in the Old Testament*. CUP, Cambridge, 1985, pp. 4–5. Also noted in Drane, *Introducing the Old Testament*, p. 247.

14 Rex Mason, *Propaganda and Subversion in the Old Testament*. SPCK, London, 1997, pp. 9–10.

15 S. Dalley, *Myths from Mesopotamia*. Oxford University Press, Oxford, 1989, pp. 228–77.

16 Day, *God's Conflict*, pp. 7–8, 16–17.

17 Bright, *History of Israel*, p. 88.

18 Gordon J. Wenham, *Genesis 1—15*. Word Books, Waco, 1987, pp. *xxxvii–xxxviii*.

19 Wenham, *Genesis 1—15*, p. 1.

20 Trigo, *Creation and History*, p. 93.

21 David Atkinson, *The Message of Genesis 1—11*. IVP, Leicester, 1990, p. 16.

22 Psalms 18.15; 29.3–4, 10–11; 77.16–18; 93.3–4; 104.6–9.

23 Psalms 74.12–17; 89.9–13; and Isaiah 27.1; 51.9–11; Job 7.12.

24 Stanley Jaki, *Genesis 1 Through the Ages*. Thomas More Press, London, 1992, pp. 13–14.

25 Jaki.

26 See note 11 in Chapter 1.

27 For a fuller discussion of these points see Wenham, *Genesis 1—15*, pp. 37–8.

28 See Wenham, *Genesis 1—15*, pp. 159–67, for a detailed discussion of these points.

29 Jaki, *Genesis 1 Through the Ages*, p. 22.

30 Artur Weiser, *The Psalms*. SCM Press, London, 1962, p. 666.

31 Leslie C. Allen, *Psalms 101—150*. Word Books, Waco, 1983, p. 31.

32 John Day (*Psalms*, JSOT, Sheffield, 1990, p. 41) draws out the striking parallels with Genesis 1, which he believes is dependent on Psalm 104. He supports this by noting that the psalm has a more primitive understanding of the conflict with chaos waters (104.5–9; see also Genesis 1.6–10); and the psalm uses the mythological name, Leviathan, while Genesis speaks of sea monsters (104.26; see also Genesis 1.24).

33 Allen, *Psalms 101—150*, p. 316.

34 Daniel 3.52–90, Septuagint reading.

35 Mark 4.1–34.

36 Acts 17.24–6.

37 Mason, *Propaganda and Subversion*, pp. 8–9.

38 Mason, *Propaganda and Subversion*, p. 10.

39 Psalm 24.1.

40 Claus Westermann, *Genesis 1—11.* SPCK, London, 1984, pp. 64–5.

41 Weiser, *The Psalms*, p. 55.

42 Compare Hosea 2.16.

43 Compare Zephaniah 1.5.

44 Day, *God's Conflict*, p. 189.

45 Psalms 77.16–18; 89.9–10; Isaiah 51.9–11, and compare 43.15–17.

46 Drane, *Introducing the Old Testament*, p. 248.

47 Ezekiel 16.17.

48 R.E. Clements, *Old Testament Theology: A Fresh Approach.* Marshall, Morgan & Scott, London, 1978, p. 60.

49 Exodus 7.10–12, 22; 8.7 etc.

50 Isaiah 40.12–14, 18–28; 41.21–4.

51 Genesis 1.14–19.

52 Trigo, *Creation and History*, pp. 102–3.

53 Trigo, *Creation and History*, p. 103.

54 Clements, *Old Testament Theology*, p. 77.

3 Creation as an Act of the Covenant God of Biblical Faith

1 Genesis 9.14–15.

2 Pedro Trigo, *Creation and History.* Burns & Oates, Tunbridge Wells, 1992, p. 88.

3 Walter Brueggemann, *Genesis.* John Knox Press, Atlanta, 1982, p. 1.

4 Claus Westermann, *Genesis 1—11.* SPCK, London, 1984, p. 52.

5 Brueggeman, *Genesis*, pp. 12–13.

6 Gordon Wenham, *Genesis 1—15.* Word Books, Waco, 1987, p. xxxiv.

7 See Genesis 3.5; 11.6. Brueggemann, *Genesis*, p. 14.

8 Ephesians 1.9–10.

9 Brueggemann, *Genesis*, p. 18.

10 Trigo, *Creation and History*, p. 95.

11 Stanley L. Jaki, *Genesis 1 Through the Ages.* Thomas More Press, London, 1992, pp. 27–8.

12 Trigo, *Creation and History*, p. 97.

13 K.-H. Bernhardt, with J. Bergmann, G.J. Botterweck, & H. Ringgren, 'bara" *Theological Dictionary of the Old Testament Vol. III.* Eerdmans, Grand Rapids, 1978, pp. 242–9.

14 Genesis 1.1.

15 Genesis 2.3–4.

16 Ellen van Wolde, *Stories of the Beginning: Genesis 1—11 and Other Creation Stories.* SCM Press, London, 1996, p. 19.

17 Westermann, *Genesis 1—11*, p. 87.

18 Westermann, *Genesis 1—11*, p. 88.

19 P.J. Wiseman (*Clues to Creation in Genesis*, Marshall, Morgan & Scott, London 1977, pp. 115ff.) and Wenham (*Genesis 1—15*, p. 7) draw attention to the correspondences between days 1 and 4, 2 and 5, 3 and 6; the events of the last three days being parallel with the first three:

day 1	Light	day 4	Luminaries
day 2	Sky	day 5	Birds and Fish
day 3	Land (plants)	day 6	Animals and Human beings (plants for food)
day 7	Sabbath		

With this arrangement, as I have shown elsewhere (*In the Beginning God: Modern Science and the Doctrine of Creation*, Regent's Park College and Macon, Smyth & Helwys, Oxford, 1994, p. 112, Figure 5.1), the Genesis 1 account of creation has a marked degree of agreement with the cosmological and geological history.

20 Brueggemann, *Genesis*, pp. 26–7.

21 Van Wolde, *Stories of the Beginning*, p. 15; Wenham, *Genesis 1—15*, p. 7.

22 Compare Revelation 4.

23 Wenham, *Genesis 1—15*, p. 37.

24 David Atkinson, *The Message of Genesis 1—11*. IVP, Leicester, 1990, pp. 37–41.

25 Brueggemann, *Genesis*, p. 37.

26 Dietrich Bonhoeffer, *Creation and Fall*. SCM Press, London, 1959, p. 42.

27 Westermann, *Genesis 1—11*, p. 192.

28 Bonhoeffer, *Creation and Fall*, p. 46.

29 Rex Mason, *Old Testament Pictures of God*. Regent's Park College and Macon, Smyth & Helwys, Oxford, 1993, p. 34.

30 Mason, *Old Testament Pictures of God*, p. 35.

31 See Hosea 11 and Isaiah 66.13.

32 Wenham, *Genesis 1—15*, p. 90.

33 Brueggemann, *Genesis*, p. 52.

34 Wenham, *Genesis 1—15*, p. 156.

35 Van Wolde, *Stories of the Beginning*, p. 123.

36 Van Wolde, *Stories of the Beginning*, p. 120.

37 Brueggemann, *Genesis*, pp. 74–5.

38 Van Wolde, *Stories of the Beginning*, pp. 132–6.

39 As in Genesis 1.31.

40 Brueggemann, *Genesis*, p. 78.

41 Atkinson, *The Message of Genesis 1—11*, p. 155.

42 Atkinson, *The Message of Genesis 1—11*, p. 166.

43 Westermann, *Genesis 1—11*, p. 476.

44 Van Wolde, *Stories of the Beginning*, p. 174.

45 John Day, *Psalms*. JSOT, Sheffield, 1990, p. 40.

46 Psalm 95.1–5.

47 Artur Weiser, *The Psalms*. SCM Press, London, 1962, p. 60.

48 See pages 15, 20–1.

49 Leslie C. Allen, *Psalms 101—150*. Word Books, Waco, 1983, p. 28.

50 For further discussion see John Day, *God's Conflict with the Dragon and the Sea: Echoes of a Canaanite Myth in the Old Testament*. Cambridge University Press, Cambridge, 1985, pp. 1–17, especially p. 7.

51 See Genesis 2.15; 3.23.

52 See Genesis 1.14.

53 See Genesis 2.7; 6.17.

54 Weiser, *The Psalms*, p. 670.

55 As in the theophany at Sinai (Exodus 19.16–19).

56 Allen, *Psalms 101—150*, pp. 313–17.

57 See Psalm 19.1.

58 Weiser, *The Psalms*, p. 838.

59 Jaki, *Genesis 1 Through the Ages*, p. 283.

60 Compare Ezra 3; 6.19–22; Isaiah 61.4–11; and also the use of this Psalm by the three men in the furnace in the Septuagint reading of Daniel 3.52–90.

61 See Exodus 19.

62 See Genesis 2 and 9.

63 David Atkinson, *The Message of Job*, IVP, Leicester, 1991, pp. 145–6.

64 Mark 8.17–21.

65 Gustavo Gutierrez (*On Job: God Talk and the Suffering of the Innocent*, Claretian Publications, 1986, p. 74), quoted in Sean McDonagh, *The Greening of the Church*. Geoffrey Chapman, London, 1990, p. 153.

66 J. Gerald Janzen, *Job*. John Knox, Atlanta, 1985, p. 229.

67 Janzen, *Job*, p. 227.

68 Atkinson (*The Message of Job*, p. 152) notes that in Job 38 and 39 very little of creation is in human control and a great deal of God's creation is secret and not open to human power and human competence. This might create a great deal of fear, but God's power is demonstrated through an examination of two frightening creatures: the beast and the dragon, Behemoth and Leviathan of the pagan myths. These are fearful mysteries that Job is powerless to control. Yet even the most monstrous and frightening are under God's control.

69 Atkinson, *The Message of Job*, p. 161.

70 Isaiah 55.9.

71 Atkinson, *The Message of Job*, p. 155.

72 1 Corinthians 3.5–7.

73 Margot Kassmann, 'Covenant, Praise and Justice in Creation: Five Bible studies', in

David Hallman (ed), *Ecotheology: Voices from South and North*. WCC, Geneva, and Orbis, Maryknoll, 1994, p. 44.

74 Genesis 1; Psalm 33.6.

75 Renthy Keitzar, 'Creation and Restoration: Three Biblical reflections', in Hallman (ed), *Ecotheology*, p. 61.

76 Hebrews 2.5–9.

77 John 3.16.

78 Day, *God's Conflict*, p. 61.

79 Isaiah 42.5; 43.1–3; 44.24b–28.

80 Gerhard von Rad, *Old Testament Theology, Volume One*. SCM Press, London, 1975, pp. 138–9.

81 Psalms 46.2–3; 74.13–14; 89.9–10; and Job 3.8; 7.12; and also Isaiah 51.9–10.

82 Von Rad, *Old Testament Theology, Volume One*, p. 151.

83 See also Proverbs 3.19–20; 8.22–31; 14.31; 20.12; etc.

84 Von Rad, *Old Testament Theology, Volume One*, p. 141.

85 Genesis 9.8–14.

86 Compare 1 Peter 3.20–1, with its reference to Christian baptism.

4 Star-gazers Tell Their Stories, Old and New

1 Matthew 2.2.

2 T.S. Eliot, *Selected Poems*. Faber & Faber, London, 1961, pp. 97–8.

3 Stephen W. Hawking, *A Brief History of Time*. Bantam Press, London and New York, 1988, p. 175.

4 Paul Davies, *The Mind of God*. Simon & Schuster, New York and London, 1992, p. 232.

5 J.O. Urmson, *The Concise Encyclopedia of Western Philosophy and Philosophers*. London, Hutchinson, 1960, pp. 28–51.

6 Quoted by Peter W. Francis, 'Exploration of the Solar System' in G.C. Brown, C.J. Hawkesworth & R.C.L.Wilson (eds), *Understanding the Earth: A New Synthesis*. Cambridge University Press, Cambridge, 1992, p. 3.

7 George Smoot & Keay Davidson, *Wrinkles in Time: The Imprint of Creation*. Abacus, London, 1993, p. 2.

8 Smoot and Davidson, *Wrinkles in Time*, p. 9.

9 Stanley L. Jaki, *Genesis 1 Through the Ages*. Thomas More Press, London, 1992, p. 182.

10 Paul Thagard, *Conceptual Revolutions*. Princeton University Press, Princeton, 1992, p. 3.

11 For use of the term 'paradigm shift' see T.S. Kuhn, *The Structure of Scientific Revolutions*. Phoenix Books, Chicago & London, 1962.

12 Thagard, *Conceptual Revolutions*, p. 6.

13 John Hedley Brooke, *Science and Religion: Some Historical Perspectives*. Cambridge University Press, Cambridge, 1991, p. 18.

14 Brooke, *Science and Religion*, p. 28.

15 Smoot and Davidson, *Wrinkles in Time*, p. 24.

16 D. Wilkinson, *God, the Big Bang and Stephen Hawking*. Monarch, Tunbridge Wells, 1993, p. 43.

17 A. Tilby, *Science and the Soul*. SPCK, London, 1992, p. 70.

18 Einstein quoted in A. Tilby, *Science and the Soul*, p. 72, and P. Davies, *The Mind of God*, Simon & Schuster, New York and London, 1992, p. 148.

19 Thagard, *Conceptual Revolutions*, pp. 223–4.

20 Smoot and Davidson, *Wrinkles in Time*, p. 36.

21 Smoot and Davidson, *Wrinkles in Time*, p. 51.

22 For a full discussion see Roger Penrose, *The Emperor's New Mind*. Oxford University Press, Oxford, 1989, pp. 302–47.

23 Stuart Ross Taylor, 'The Origin of the Earth' in G.C. Brown, C.J. Hawkesworth & R.C.L. Wilson (eds), *Understanding the Earth: a New Synthesis*. Cambridge University Press, Cambridge, 1992, p. 26.

24 See John Polkinghorne, *One World: the Interaction of Science and Theology*. SPCK, London, 1986, p. 56.

25 Stuart Ross Taylor, 'The Origin of the Earth', p. 27.

26 Stuart Ross Taylor, 'The Origin of the Earth', p. 43.

27 For further discussion on these discoveries see Smoot and Davidson, *Wrinkles in Time*, pp. 58–60.

28 Hawking, *A Brief History of Time*, pp. 49–50.

29 Smoot and Davidson, *Wrinkles in Time*, p. 272–3.

30 Smoot and Davidson, *Wrinkles in Time*, p. 278.

31 Smoot and Davidson, *Wrinkles in Time*, p. 291.

32 For a fuller discussion of these points see: Paul Davies, *The Mind of God*; Roger Penrose, *The Emperor's New Mind*; John Barrow, *Theories of Everything* (OUP, Oxford, 1990); and my own work, *In the Beginning God: Modern Science and the Christian Doctrine of Creation* (Regent's Park College and Macon, Smyth & Helwys, Oxford, 1994).

33 For works on chaos theory see J. Gleick, *Chaos* (Cardinal, 1987) and *Chaos: Making a New Science* (Viking, New York, 1988). Also see I. Stewart, *Does God Play Dice?* (Blackwell, Oxford,1989) and J.T. Houghton, 'New Ideas of Chaos in Physics', *Science and Christian Belief*, 1 (1990), pp. 41–51.

34 See Paul S. Fiddes, *The Creative Suffering of God*. Oxford University Press, Oxford, 1988, pp. 61, 63ff.

35 Smoot and Davidson, *Wrinkles in Time*, p. 293.

36 Smoot and Davidson, *Wrinkles in Time*, p. 296.

37 Benjamin Gal-Or, *Cosmology, Physics and Philosophy*. Springer Verlag, New York, 1981, p. 5.

38 Jaki, *Genesis 1 Through the Ages*, p. 253.

39 The steady state theory gave an eternal ground to the existence of the universe and it has been suggested that it was one of the background cultural influences that led theologians like John Robinson to regard God less as personal than as 'the ultimate reality', and Tillich to suggest that God was not exterior to the universe but 'the ground of our being'. There is a warning here for all theologians, that they should take care in aligning theology with scientific theories which are constantly being revised as new facts come to light.

40 For Hawking (*A Brief History of Time*), to be left with merely a 'singularity' as the solution to the beginning of the universe would be a frustration, as a singularity is the ultimate unknowable. The real philosophical problem with the Big Bang is that it is a one-off happening, an anomaly. It is impossible to get behind it or before it. Scientists have tried to cope with this dilemma by suggesting cycles of bangs and crunches, or parallel universes. There is a widespread desire to get away from an idea of uniqueness. This desire is the motivation behind the search for a unifying of the four forces that govern the universe: gravity, electromagnetism, and the weak and strong nuclear forces. Such a grand unifying theory is believed by some to be the ultimate answer.

41 Keith Ward, *God, Chance and Necessity*. One World, Oxford, 1996, pp. 16–17.

42 Ward, *God, Chance and Necessity*, p. 18.

43 Smoot and Davidson, *Wrinkles in Time*, p. 295.

5 The Earth Gives up Her Dead – Stories of Fossils and Favoured Species

1 Genesis 1.20.

2 G.Y. Craig, *The 1785 Abstract of James Hutton's Theory of the Earth*. Scottish Academic Press, Edinburgh, 1987, p. 4.

3 Subsequently revised on many occasions, especially after the publication of Darwin's *Origin of the Species* in 1859, when he included sections dealing with evolution.

4 Quoted by Stanley Jaki, *Genesis 1 Through the Ages*. Thomas More Press, London, 1992, p. 227.

5 William Buckland, *Geology and Mineralogy in Reference to Natural Theology*. 1836; reprinted by Carey, Lea & Blanchard, Philadelphia, 1937.

6 Stuart Ross Taylor, 'The Origin of the Earth' in G.C. Brown, C.J. Hawkesworth & R.C.L. Wilson (eds), *Understanding the Earth: A New Synthesis*. Cambridge University Press, Cambridge, 1992, pp. 36–7.

7 Brian F. Windley, *The Evolving Continents*. John Wiley, Chichester, 1995, p. 1.

8 Windley, *The Evolving Continents*, p. 6.

9 A minor movement (a couple of millimetres or less) along a fracture in the earth's

crust will produce a major earthquake. The last major movement along the San Andreas Fault was the great San Francisco earthquake of 1906. From 1906 to 1999 is 93 years, which at 3 cm/year is almost three metres. There is a major earthquake waiting to occur!

10 Chris J. Hawkesworth & Peter van Calsteren, 'Geological Time' in G.C. Brown, C.J. Hawkesworth & R.C.L. Wilson (eds), *Understanding the Earth: a New Synthesis*. Cambridge University Press, Cambridge, 1992, p. 135.

11 Windley, *The Evolving Continents*, p. 418.

12 Windley, *The Evolving Continents*, p. 422.

13 See Windley *The Evolving Continents*, pp. 426–7 and Simon Conway Morris, 'The Early Evolution of Life' in G.C. Brown, C.J. Hawkesworth & R.C.L.Wilson (eds), *Understanding the Earth*, pp. 437–9 for a fuller discussion of these points.

14 For a detailed consideration of the greenhouse effect and global warming see John Houghton, *Global Warming* (Lion, Oxford, 1994). We shall also return to this subject in Chapter 8, when we consider a theology for Earthkeeping.

15 Cesare Emiliani, *Planet Earth: Cosmology, Geology, and the Evolution of Life and Environment*. Cambridge University Press, Cambridge, 1992, 1995, p. 371.

16 In the 1930s J.B.S. Haldane suggested that organic compounds formed in the early atmosphere of the earth and eventually found their way into the oceans, which formed a hot 'soup' where these compounds could grow. This would form a non-oxidizing or reducing environment. The great leap forward in the study of the origin of life came with the work of S.L. Miller in 1953, who demonstrated in an experiment that the amino acids, purines, and pyramidines could be produced naturally in such a reducing environment. Miller applied electrical discharges to a mixed 'atmosphere' including methane, ammonia, and water vapour, and produced a number of organic compounds. It was considered that as a result there would be a build-up of organic compounds in the oceans, which would provide a 'nutrient broth' in which the first living organisms developed. This led scientists to believe that the earth's primitive atmosphere was a reducing one, with carbon present in the form of methane. However, though today no one doubts the validity of Miller's experiments, there is now considerable doubt over the composition of the atmosphere that was assumed.

17 Simon Conway Morris, 'The Early Evolution of Life' in G.C. Brown, C.J. Hawkesworth & R.C.L. Wilson (eds), *Understanding the Earth*, p. 438.

18 L.V. Berkner & L.C. Marshall, 'Oxygen and Evolution' in I.G. Gass, P.J. Smith & R.C.L. Wilson, *Understanding the Earth*. Open University, Artemis Press, Sussex, 1971, pp. 143–9.

19 Berkner and Marshall, 'Oxygen and Evolution'.

20 J.E. Lovelock, *Gaia: A New Look at Life on Earth*. Oxford University Press, Oxford, 1987, p. 10.

21 Paul Thagard, *Conceptual Revolutions*. Princeton University Press, 1992, p. 133.

22 For Paley's understanding of the individual divine design of animals and plants and the finding of a watch while walking on the heath indicating a watch-maker, see William Paley, *Natural Theology*. 1802, reprinted in R. Lyman (ed.), *The Works of William Paley* (London, 1925).

23 Paul Thagard, *Conceptual Revolutions*, p. 136.

24 R.J. Berry, *God and the Biologist*. IVP, Leicester, 1996, p. 60.

25 Berry, *God and the Biologist*, p. 64.

26 R. Dawkins, *The Blind Watchmaker*. Longmans, London, 1986.

27 Dawkins, *The Blind Watchmaker*, pp. 317–18.

28 R.J. Berry, *God and the Biologist*, p. 31.

29 R.J. Berry, *Adam and the Ape*. Falcon, London, 1975.

30 Berry, *God and the Biologist*, p. 54.

31 Simon Conway Morris, 'The Early Evolution of Life', p. 439.

32 Stephen Jay Gould (*Wonderful Life: The Burgess Shale and the Nature of History*, Hutchinson Radius, London, 1990) through his work on the Cambrian (530 million years BP) Burgess Shale of British Columbia, draws attention to the wide variety of classes and phyla that are present in the Burgess Shale, leading him to suggest that 'the maximum range of anatomical possibilities arises with the first rush of diversification ... Later history is a tale of restriction, as most of these early experiments succumb and life settles down to generating endless variants upon a few surviving models' (p. 47). Gould says that Darwin saw competition under natural selection, with the better-adapted species winning, and so for Darwin contingency is the primary support to evolution (p. 300). Yet Gould maintains that nature was not as smoothly ordered as Darwin suggested, that large scale catastrophic changes in environment have left their mark. He concludes that the Burgess Shale suggests a pattern of maximum diversity at the bottom, with contingency leading to proliferation along certain lines only – a 'Christmas tree, bottom heavy, evolutionary tree'.

33 Ruth Page, *God and the Web of Creation*. SCM Press, London, 1996, p. 240.

34 David Atkinson, *The Message of Genesis 1—11*. IVP, Leicester, 1990, pp. 30–1.

35 Jacques Monod, *Chance and Necessity*. Collins, London, 1972, p. 67.

36 Hebrews 11.3. Berry, *God and the Biologist*, p. 6.

37 It is exemplified by Jacques Monod's *Chance and Necessity* (1970; English translation Collins, London, 1972). Monod wrote that 'Chance *alone* is at the source of every innovation, of all creation in the biosphere. Pure chance, absolutely free but blind, [is] at the very root of the stupendous edifice of evolution' (p. 110) and that 'holists totally lack understanding of scientific method and of the crucial role analysis plays in it' (p. 80).

38 For further discussion see Nancey Murphy, *Reconciling Theology and Science*. Pandora Press, Kitchener, and Herald Press, Scottdale, 1997, pp. 13ff.

39 Murphy, *Reconciling Theology and Science*, p. 65.

40 Murphy, *Reconciling Theology and Science*, p. 78.

41 R. Penrose, *The Emperor's New Mind*. Oxford University Press, Oxford, 1989.

42 Penrose, *The Emperor's New Mind*, p. 447.

6 What Sort of God and How Has God Been Perceived by Human Beings?

1 Job 38.4.

2 Peter Atkins, speaking at the annual festival of the British Association for the Advancement of Science, as reported in the *Electronic Telegraph*, issue 476, Wednesday 11 September 1996.

3 Paul Vallely, 'Creative tension – Evolution still on Trial' in *The Independent* newspaper, Tuesday 8 April 1997.

4 John Hedley Brooke, *Science and Religion: Some Historical Perspectives*. Cambridge University Press, Cambridge, 1991, pp. 34–5.

5 Brooke, *Science and Religion*, p. 36.

6 Brooke, *Science and Religion*, pp. 44ff.

7 Nancey Murphy, *Reconciling Theology and Science: A Radical Reformation Perspective*. Pandora Press, Kitchener, and Herald Press, Scottdale, 1997, p. 65.

8 Steven Weinberg, who is Professor of Theoretical Physics at the University of Austin, Texas, and a Nobel Prize winner with Abdus Salam on the symmetry of forces in the early universe, declared in his book *The First Three Minutes* (Bantam Press, 1979) that the more the universe seems comprehensible, the more it also seems pointless. Weinberg believes that doing science gives human beings some sense of grace in the midst of the tragedy of being trapped in a hostile world. From his perspective it would appear that doing science gives point to living, but the discoveries thus made present existence as pointless. Such a state of affairs would seem to be a recipe for suicide. (Quoted by Angela Tilby in *Science and the Soul*. SPCK, London, 1992, pp. 20–1 and 262.)

9 Colin Brown, *Philosophy and the Christian Faith*. Tyndale, Leicester, 1969, p. 26.

10 David Hume, *Dialogues Concerning Natural Religion* (1779), reprinted in the Hafner Library of Classics (Hafner, New York, 1948), p. 47ff. (Chapter VII).

11 W.H. Walsh, 'Immanuel Kant' in P. Edwards (ed.), *The Encyclopedia of Philosophy*. Macmillan & The Free Press, New York; Collier Macmillan, London, 1967, p. 316.

12 L. Newbigin, *The Other Side of 1984: Questions for the Churches*. WCC, Geneva, 1983, p. 60.

13 Eileen Conn and James Stewart (eds), *Visions of Creation*. Godsfield Press, Alresford, 1995, pp. 2–3.

14 Howard A. Snyder, *Earth Currents: the Struggle for the World's Soul*. Abingdon Press, Nashville, 1995, pp. 177–9.

15 J.E. Lovelock, *Gaia: A New Look at Life on Earth*. Oxford University Press, Oxford, 1987, p. 10.

16 P. Davies, *The Mind of God*. Simon & Schuster, New York and London, 1992.

17 S.W. Hawking, *A Brief History of Time*. Bantam Press, London and New York, 1988, p. 171.

18 While entropy increases in the universe system as a whole, complex life-forms develop in a manner that seems to run counter to this pattern, by taking in energy in a low entropy form and *discarding* it in a high entropy form. The human body, for example, takes in energy in the low entropy form of food and oxygen, and discards it in the high entropy form of heat, CO_2, and excreta. In this way, suggests Penrose, we are constantly fighting against the second law of thermodynamics. Low entropy energy from the sun is converted through photosynthesis in plants into organized structures, while high entropy radiant heat is given off into space. Such a source of low entropy energy is vital for complex organisms to develop. This phenomenon supplies us with another plank in the argument that the universe shows a remarkable degree of 'fine tuning'. As Penrose remarks, 'For some reason, the universe was created in a very special (low entropy) state.' R. Penrose, *The Emperor's New Mind*, p. 339.

19 R.J. Berry, 'Green Religion and Green Science' in David Atkinson, *Pastoral Ethics*. Lynx, Oxford, 1994, p. 132.

20 Physicists tell us that to produce carbon, hydrogen, nitrogen, oxygen, and phosphorus, all vital for life, requires nuclear reactions in the interior of stars, which are dispersed into space during a supernova explosion at the end of a star's life. Almost all the carbon in our bodies will have such an astral history. It is estimated that it would take over 10 billion years, from the Big Bang, of such stellar alchemy to provide the necessary precursors of life. J.D. Barrow, *Theories of Everything*, p. 165.

21 Nancey Murphy, *Reconciling Theology and Science*, pp. 72–4.

22 J. Polkinghorne, *Science and Creation*. SPCK, London, 1988, pp. 47–8.

23 J. Monod, *Chance and Necessity*. Collins, London, 1972.

24 Job 38; Isaiah 40.18–28; 42.5; John 5.17.

25 Ecclesiastes 1.4–7.

26 Job 38.31–3.

27 Isaiah 40.25–6.

28 1 Corinthians 14.33.

29 Matthew 16.2–3; Luke 12.54–6.

30 John 1.1–18; Hebrews 1.1–3; Colossians 1.15–20.

31 Romans 8.19–23; Revelation 4—5 and 21—22.

32 S.W. Hawking, *A Brief History of Time*. Bantam Press, London and New York, 1988.

33 J. Hick, *Arguments for the Existence of God*. Macmillan, London, 1971, pp. 33–6, 46, 108–16.

34 P. Davies, *God and the New Physics* (Dent, London, 1983); *The Mind of God* (Simon & Schuster, New York and London, 1992).

35 L. Campbell and W. Garnett, *The Life of James Clerk Maxwell*. Macmillan, London, 1882, pp. 392, 394. This is also quoted in Stanley L. Jaki, *Genesis 1 Through the Ages*. Thomas More Press, London, 1992, pp. 234–5.

36 E. Brunner, *The Christian Doctrine of Creation and Redemption*. Lutterworth Press, London, 1952, p. 18.

37 Ruth Page, *God and the Web of Creation*. SCM Press, London, 1996, p. 38.

38 K.R. Popper, *A World of Propensities*. Thoemmes, Bristol, 1990, p. 12.

39 J.B. Phillips, *Your God is Too Small*. Epworth Press, London, 1952.

40 Ruth Page, *God and the Web of Creation*, p. 38.

41 John Macquarrie, *Principles of Christian Theology*. SCM Press, London, 1977, p. 218.

42 Keith Ward, *Religion and Creation* (Oxford, Clarendon Press, 1996), pp. 54–5.

43 Macquarrie, *Principles of Christian Theology*, p. 221.

7 Letting the Stories be Heard – Listening to Each Other

1 Romans 1.20.

2 R.D. Jastrow, *Reader's Digest* (Reader's Digest Ltd, October 1980) p. 57, quoted in D. Wilkinson, *God, the Big Bang and Stephen Hawking*. Monarch, Tunbridge Wells, 1993, p. 71.

3 George Smoot & Keay Davidson, *Wrinkles in Time: The Imprint of Creation*. Abacus, London, 1993, p. 297.

4 Nancey Murphy, *Reconciling Theology and Science: A Radical Reformation Perspective*. Pandora Press, Kitchener, and Herald Press, Scottdale, 1997.

5 Howard A. Snyder, *Earth Currents: the Struggle for the World's Soul*. Abingdon Press, Nashville, 1995, p. 13.

6 Snyder, *Earth Currents*, p. 19.

7 S.W. Hawking, *A Brief History of Time*. Bantam Press, London and New York, 1988, p. 78.

8 J.D. Barrow, *Theories of Everything*. Oxford University Press, Oxford, 1990, p. 204.

9 Barrow, *Theories of Everything*, p. 204.

10 Objective observation has been questioned. For example, Michael Polanyi (*Personal Knowledge*, Routledge & Kegan Paul, London, 1958) has emphasized the part played by personal judgement in scientific research. We have to recognize that scientific experiment or observation can be both fact-laden and theory-laden; the theory may often be in the mind of the observer before they conduct the experiment; and for any collection of data there may be more than one possible solution. Yet for all this the one goal that drives scientific investigations is the desire for knowledge, to understand better the way the world is.

11 Smoot & Davidson, *Wrinkles in Time*, pp. 278ff.

12 Richard Dawkins, *The Blind Watchmaker*. Longmans, London, 1986 – see especially pp. 21ff., 37ff. Also Stephen Jay Gould, *Wonderful Life: The Burgess Shale and the Nature of History*. Hutchinson Radius, London, 1990, p. 321.

13 J.D. Barrow, *Theories of Everything*, pp. 23–9.

14 J. Hick, *Arguments for the Existence of God*. Macmillan, London, 1971, p. 46.

15 See Roger Penrose, *The Emperor's New Mind*. Oxford University Press, Oxford, 1989. Also John Puddefoot, *God and the Mind Machine*. SPCK, London, 1996.

16 Genesis 1.27.

17 1 Corinthians 13.12.

18 Genesis 2.7.

19 J. Polkinghorne, *Science and Creation*. SPCK, London, 1988, pp. 1–2.

20 C. Westermann, *Genesis 1—11*. SPCK, London, 1984, p. 84.

21 J.D. Weaver, *In the Beginning God: Modern Science and the Christian Doctrine of Creation*. Regent's Park College and Macon, Smyth & Helwys, Oxford, 1994, pp. 111–14 and Figure 5.1.

22 Genesis 8.18—9.7.

23 Romans 8.19, 22–23.

24 L. Newbigin, *Foolishness to the Greeks: The Gospel and Western Culture*. SPCK, London, 1986, pp. 18–19.

25 Dietrich Bonhoeffer, *Creation and Fall*. SCM Press, London, 1959, p. 14.

26 John Hick, *Evil and the God of Love*. Collins, Glasgow, 1979, p. 317.

27 Paul Fiddes, *The Creative Suffering of God*. Clarendon Press, Oxford, 1988, p. 45.

28 Fiddes, *The Creative Suffering of God*, pp. 210ff.

29 Quoted in Fiddes, *The Creative Suffering of God*, p. 263.

30 Revelation 21.

31 Fiddes, *The Creative Suffering of God*, pp. 105–6.

32 Exodus 14.

33 David Atkinson, *The Message of Genesis 1—11*. IVP, Leicester, 1990, p. 39.

34 J. Hick, *Arguments for the Existence of God*, p. 106.

35 Fiddes, *The Creative Suffering of God*, pp. 94ff.

36 Murphy, *Reconciling Theology and Science*, p. 82.

37 Sean McDonagh, *The Greening of the Church*. Geoffrey Chapman, London, 1990, pp. 244–5.

8 A Theology for Earthkeeping

1 Genesis 2.15.

2 Steve Turner, *Up to Date: Poems 1968–1982*. Hodder & Stoughton, London, 1983, p. 91.

3 Sean McDonagh, *The Greening of the Church*. Geoffrey Chapman, London, 1990, p. 73.

4 For detailed discussion of the impact of global warming, see John Houghton, *Global Warming*. Lion, Oxford, 1994.

5 Howard Snyder, *Earth Currents: the Struggle for the World's Soul*. Abingdon Press, Nashville, 1995, p. 242.

6 McDonagh, *The Greening of the Church*, p. 9.

7 McDonagh, *The Greening of the Church*, p. 12.

8 Snyder, *Earth Currents*, p. 84.

9 R.P. Moss, 'Environment' in David Atkinson & David Field (eds), *New Dictionary of Christian Ethics and Pastoral Theology*. IVP, Leicester, 1995, p. 349.

10 R.P. Moss in Atkinson & Field, p. 350.

11 R.J. Berry, 'Green Religion and Green Science' in David Atkinson, *Pastoral Ethics*. Lynx, Oxford, 1994, p. 132.

12 J.E. Lovelock, *Gaia: A New Look at Life on Earth*. Oxford University Press, Oxford, 1987.

13 John Houghton, *Global Warming*, p. 117.

14 R.J. Berry in David Atkinson, *Pastoral Ethics*, p. 124.

15 Timothy Chester, *Awakening to a World of Need*. IVP, Leicester, 1993, p. 71.

16 R.J. Berry in David Atkinson, *Pastoral Ethics*, p. 137.

17 K.C. Abraham, 'A Theological Response to the Ecological Crisis' in David Hallam (ed.), *Ecotheology: Voices from South and North*. WCC, Geneva and Orbis, Maryknoll, 1994, p. 75.

18 Job 38; Isaiah 40.18–28; 42.5; John 5.17.

19 Genesis 2.7.

20 Job 38.31–3.

21 Isaiah 40.25–6.

22 Romans 1.20.

23 Psalms 19; 104.

24 Matthew 16.2–3; Luke 12.54–5.

25 Acts 14.17; 17.24–6.

26 Psalm 24.1.

27 Psalm 115.16.

28 Genesis 1.26, 28.

29 Leviticus 25.23; compare Luke 4.19.

30 Genesis 6.19.

31 Genesis 9.8–14.

32 Compare 1 Peter 3.20–1 – Christian baptism.

33 Romans 8.23.

34 Sean McDonagh, *The Greening of the Church*, p. 127.

35 Robert McAfee Brown, *Gustavo Gutierrez: An Introduction to Liberation Theology.* Orbis, New York, 1990, pp. 56–7.

36 Romans 8.18–23.

37 John 10.10.

38 1 Corinthians 11.

39 Luke 4.18–19.

40 Clare Palmer, 'Stewardship: A Case Study in Environmental Ethics' in Ian Ball, Margaret Goodall, Clare Palmer & John Reader (eds), *The Earth Beneath: A Critical Guide to Green Theology.* SPCK, London, 1992, p. 68.

41 P.N. Hillyer, 'Stewardship' in David Atkinson & David Field (eds), *New Dictionary of Christian Ethics and Pastoral Theology.* IVP, Leicester, 1995, p. 814.

42 Robin Attfield, *Environmental Philosophy: Principles and Prospects.* Avebury, Aldershot, 1994, pp. 225–6.

43 K.C. Abraham, in David Hallmann, *Ecotheology,* pp. 68–9.

44 Paul Haffner, 'A Christian Ecology' in Robert Whelan, Joseph Kirwan & Paul Haffner, *The Cross and the Rain Forest: A Critique of Radical Green Spirituality.* Eerdmans, Grand Rapids, 1996, p. 126.

45 Romans 8.19–22.

46 Margot Kassmann, 'Covenant, Praise and Justice in Creation' in David Hallman, *Ecotheology,* p. 49.

9. A Doctrine of Creation

1 Psalm 19.1.

2 John 1.1–5.

3 Colossians 1.15–20.

4 Colossians 1.17.

5 Romans 8.19–23.

6 1 Corinthians 11.23–6; compare also Mark 14.22–5 and Matthew 26.26–9.

7 Revelation 4 and 21—22.

8 Walter Eichrodt, *Theology of the Old Testament, Volume Two.* SCM Press, London, 1967, p. 100.

9 Rex Mason, *Old Testament Pictures of God.* Regent's Park College and Macon, Smyth & Helwys, Oxford, 1993, pp. 32–3.

10 1 John 4.7–10.

11 Philippians 2.5–8; compare John 3.16.

12 Eichrodt, *Theology of the Old Testament, Volume Two,* p. 105.

13 Jürgen Moltmann, *God in Creation: An Ecological Doctrine of Creation. The Gifford Lectures 1984–1985.* SCM Press, London, 1985, pp. 74–6.

14 Moltmann, *God in Creation,* p. 13.

15 Moltmann, *God in Creation,* p. 14.

16 Moltmann, *God in Creation*, p. 211.

17 For example, Isaiah 43.18–19.

18 John Macquarrie, *Principles of Christian Theology*. SCM Press, London, 1977, pp. 217–18.

19 John 1.2; Colossians 1.15–16; Hebrews 1.2.

20 Romans 8.19, 22–3.

21 Macquarrie, *Principles of Christian Theology*, pp. 220–1.

22 Moltmann, *God in Creation*, pp. 3–4.

23 Eichrodt, *Theology of the Old Testament, Volume Two*, p. 113.

24 Eichrodt, *Theology of the Old Testament, Volume Two*, p. 101.

25 Pedro Trigo, *Creation and History*. Burns & Oates, Tunbridge Wells, 1992, p. 106.

26 Howard A. Snyder, *Earth Currents: the Struggle for the World's Soul*. Abingdon Press, Nashville, 1995, p. 243.

27 Snyder, *Earth Currents*, pp. 244–5.

28 Snyder, *Earth Currents*, p. 245.

29 Donald M. Baillie, *The Theology of the Sacraments*. Faber & Faber, London, 1957, p. 44.

30 John Calvin, *Institutes*, IV, xiv, 18, quoted by Baillie, *Theology of the Sacraments*, p. 45.

31 Matthew 6.28–30.

32 Baillie, *Theology of the Sacraments*, p. 47.

33 Ruth Page, *God and the Web of Creation*. SCM Press, London, 1996, p. 53.

34 1 John 4.7–10.

35 Page, *God and the Web of Creation*, p. 58.

36 Ellen van Wolde, *Stories of the Beginning: Genesis 1—11 and Other Creation Stories*. SCM Press, London, 1996, pp. 132–6.

37 Page, *God and the Web of Creation*, p. 61.

38 Moltmann, *God in Creation*, p. 6.

39 Leviticus 25.1–7.

40 Leviticus 25.8–55; compare Luke 4.18.

41 Keith Ward, *Religion and Creation*. Clarendon Press, Oxford, 1996, pp. 15–19.

42 Paul Fiddes, *The Creative Suffering of God*. Oxford University Press, Oxford, 1988, pp. 105–6.

43 Fiddes, *The Creative Suffering of God*, pp. 94ff.

44 Romans 8.22–3.

45 Romans 8.19–22.

46 J.E. Lovelock, *Gaia: A New Look at Life on Earth*. Oxford University Press, Oxford, 1987.

47 Robin Attfield, *Environmental Philosophy: Principles and Prospects*. Avebury, Aldershot, 1994, p. 241.

48 John Houghton, *Global Warming*. Lion, Oxford, 1994, p. 125.

49 Ward, *Religion and Creation*, pp. 45–6.

50 Ward, *Religion and Creation*, p. 46.

51 Macquarrie, *Principles of Christian Theology*, p. 220; John 1.3; Colossians 1.15–17.

52 Ward, *Religion and Creation*, pp. 54–5.

53 1 Corinthians 8.6; Ephesians 1.9ff; Colossians 1.15ff.; Hebrews 1.2–3; John 1.1–3.

54 Proverbs 8.22–31.

55 2 Corinthians 1.22; 5.5; Ephesians 1.14, and compare the end time of the Spirit, Joel 2.28.

56 Moltmann, *God in Creation*, pp. 96–8.

57 'I am in the Father and the Father is in me' (John 14.11). 'I and the Father are one' (John 10.30).

58 Moltmann, *God in Creation*, p. 77.

59 Psalm 95.1–5.

60 Psalms 19.1–2 and 97.6.

61 Psalm 8.

62 Noted by Sean McDonagh, *The Greening of the Church*. Geoffrey Chapman, London, 1990, p. 167. This is cited in Andrew Linzey & Tom Regan, *Compassion for Animals*. SPCK, London, 1988, p. 34.

63 McDonagh, *The Greening of the Church*, p. 174.

64 Einstein is quoted by Angela Tilby in *Science and the Soul* (SPCK, London 1992), p. 72, and by Paul Davies in *The Mind of God* (Simon & Schuster, New York and London, 1992), p. 148.

65 Genesis 2.1–3.

66 Psalm 95.11.

67 Hebrews 4.11.

68 David Atkinson, *The Message of Genesis 1—11*. IVP, Leicester, 1990, p. 49.

Postscript

1 This postscript is based on the Epilogue to my previous work, *In the Beginning God: Modern Science and the Christian Doctrine of Creation*. Regent's Park College and Macon, Smyth & Helwys, Oxford, 1994, p. 203.

2 Revelation 22.13.

3 A modern Celtic prayer from *The Whole Earth Shall Cry Glory: Iona Prayers by Rev. George F. MacLeod* (Wild Goose Publications, 1986), included in the collection *Daily Readings with George MacLeod*, edited by Ronald Ferguson. Fount/HarperCollins, London, 1991, pp. 42–3.

Index